Books by TOM LEA

THE BRAVE BULLS

THE WONDERFUL COUNTRY

THE KING RANCH

THE PRIMAL YOKE

THE HANDS OF CANTÚ

The Hands of Cantú

The Hands of Cantú

TOM LEA

illustrated by the author

*"Concerning horses,
in our New Spain none are equal
to those we call Ibarra Horses."*

LITTLE, BROWN AND COMPANY · BOSTON · TORONTO

Published simultaneously in Canada
by Little, Brown & Company (Canada) Limited

PRINTED IN THE UNITED STATES OF AMERICA

a
los jinetes buenos
y en especial
RMK

The
Hands of Cantú

At Coyoacán, Valley of Mexico
Day of San Blas, annᵒ Dⁱ 1580

To the distinguished SEÑOR DON VITO CANTÚ
Most Esteemed Sir:
   This letter will be delivered to your own discreet
hand and eye by a young servant of my household,
Toribio, who will forthwith place himself at your command. The boy is an orphan. We have found him of
such apt mind and demeanor that we have granted him
some advantage of instruction in letters, with other polite schooling; to the extent of allowing him the use of
our name Ibarra for a surname, which he lacked. He
shows ability with horses and rides well, I am told. I
request you to make him useful to our house and to
yourself at Acuichál.
   Now, concerning other matters:

[3]

The noble lord Don Lorenzo de Suárez, Count of Coruña, assumes here his new office and power as viceroy. We observe shiftings of influence and authority in affairs of our New Spain.

You may anticipate delay in perfection of your title to wilderness lands comprising livestock pastures named Acuichál, defined by survey already performed and recorded. Completion of title now requires the viceregal signature in the King's name, with attesting signatures of the Higher Council; and lastly will require the long journey of the authorized licentiate and his notaries to the Acuichál property, there to place you in full and final possession by ceremony performed within metes and bounds of said lands. Be not worried with the official lentitude, for I have promised you Acuichál. You shall have perfected title in token of reward for great services both to myself and to my lamented nephew, Francisco, whom God rest.

Be certain I await the fruitful opportunity to remind the noble Count of Coruña that I have expended from my own personal treasury more than 200,000 gold ducats in the discovery, conquest and pacification of our Nueva Vizcaya.

There is renewed discussion here relating to unknown realms beyond our present certain knowledge, in those terrains of the yet unvisited and yet unmeasured North. You will recall what we ourselves have known and recounted concerning the report of Nuñez Cabeza de Vaca more than forty years past. Also the lies of that friar, Marcos of Niza. Then the failure of the unfortunate Vásquez de Coronado to find anything in the North, or very little.

Now influential persons speak of those lands hopefully. Our new lord viceroy listens.

He considers the notion of authorizing an escort for a certain Franciscan missionary, now at Santa Bárbola, to go into the North for the conversion of the heathen; also for the purpose of bringing back a *dependable* report of what is found, including whatever can be ascertained about that realm supposed to contain the rich cities with the houses of great height. Of course a reverend father is seraphically suited for the glory of saving souls which the Devil holds captive. But the very zeal a friar displays in fact unsuits him, oftentimes, for the accurate reporting of other matters, such as presence or absence of minerals, *et cetera*. I could greatly wish that a gentleman soldier of your own special merit might accompany the party of religious, as captain of its escort upon its northern passage. Yet I at this time lack that degree of influence here to put forward your name with assurance of success, so I do not.

I regret that the years now begin to rob me of

strength and resource to forge events as I did in those times of my well-beloved father-in-law, our noble viceroy Don Luis de Velasco; and my gifted nephew, Don Francisco de Ibarra, with whom you explored to Paquimé so far to the north in the year '66.

I admonish you to be alert for any consequential information concerning the North, for I cannot help but believe there are wonders in these Indies we have not yet found; though I know that in some matters of great import we live as victims of rumor, or of that which we wish to believe rather than that which is the truth.

Teach the boy Toribio your own respect for truth and make him your trustworthy courier to me if there is occasion for it. Good friend Don Vito, may the hands of Our Lord and His Blessed Mother give you guard and guide.

I remain yours ever faithfully,
Diego
de Ibarra

Among those competent to judge, Don Vito Cantú was the best horseman ever seen in New Spain. All equestrian accomplishments were combined in him: as a riding master, rein-trainer and furthermore as a breeder of horses he had no equal. In an epoch when a gentleman's mettle and quality were best measured by his conduct in the saddle, at a time when the noble and enduring horse not only was the most useful animal in the daily service of man but was indeed a prime imperial weapon of conquest on this new continent of the Indies, consider what distinction belonged to Don Vito Cantú.

He was born in Andalusia, a birthplace of good horsemen, at Dehesa de Oro near the ancient Ronda. They christened him Evaristo Rodrigo Cantú, but they called him Vito. He rode horses from the time his infant hands could hold reins. Destiny made him a man

[7]

of consequence to savage spaces of a new world across an Ocean Sea: in the year 1552 he brought from Spain to the City of Mexico two Barbary stallions and five mares of exceptional worth.

I first saw him one morning during Lent of the year 1580. He came riding a gray stud up the street of the mines of San Martín. I remember how he rode, like a god of horsemanship. I remember how he looked when he dismounted at the door of the *caja*, the treasurer's office at the mines.

His hair was gray and so were his spiked mustachios. His face bore marks of hard years and hard weathers. His hat, more broadly brimmed than a bishop's, was banded with stitched leather embellished not with a plume but with the stiff tail-tip of a mountain deer. His quilted buff-leather doublet, his leathern and baize trunk hose, his tall jackboots were those of a soldier familiar with rough employment and open sky. He was armed with an iron-hilted sword; spurs with rowels long as my middle finger made a music like bells at his heels.

I stood inside the *caja* when Don Vito Cantú entered. He looked around, adjusting his sun-tightened eyes to see who was there, then bowed, proffering his ungloved hand to the royal accountant Don Cirilo Fraga. After amenities Don Cirilo, who had a mouth

[8]

Sr: don Vito Cantú

like a tight seam, granted me permission to come forward. On bent knee and kissing the hand, I put myself under the orders of Don Vito Cantú, then presented the letter I carried sealed by the signet and bearing the rubric of the Knight Commander of the Order of Santiago Don Diego de Ibarra, founder and lord of Nueva Vizcaya, owner of mines from Zacatecas to Nombre de Dios, and my own patron and protector.

Glancing at the royal accountant and saying, " — With your permission," Don Vito Cantú broke the letter's red wax seals and moved to more light by the window.

This is a good place to tell who I am.

My name is Toribio de Ibarra, but I do not know who my parents were. I was a foundling, left new born at the portal of the old Hospitál de Jesús not far from the viceroy's palace. Whether I be of Spanish or Indian blood, or of both, I do not know nor does anyone else. This has given me finally a liberation of mind, which I duly value, having no excessive position to maintain either as an inferior or as a superior envelope for a human soul. I hope it does not damage my acceptance here as a witness.

The letter I delivered was not brief. Don Vito Cantú's eyes seemed to study each line with an increasing slowness and care; his face showed no slightest change of expression. When he finished reading he refolded the letter and tucked it very securely under the sweatband of his big hat. Then he directed his eyes at me.

"So you are from the household," he said. "I lived in the house at Coyoacán. When it was yet building, many years past."

"Yes, sir. It is well known that you lived there. And remembered by all."

"How is the health of Don Diego?"

"It confines him more or less to his chair and his bed. In the great house."

"I judged so. And am profoundly sorry." He was silent, then spoke again. "Toribio. You are named thus?"

"Yes, sir."

"How old are you?"

"I am seventeen, they say."

His eyes seemed to measure me before he said, "My Captain General Don Francisco de Ibarra, whom God now rests, he was the same age when we first rode into the North. Seventeen. And a captain. Did you know that?"

"Yes, sir." I felt a sharp sense of my own unimportance.

"Ummm. How does this North appear to you? This

wilderness. Two hundred thirty leagues from Coyoacán."

"I like it." I could say nothing else.

"You will see more of it. Tell me, what class of
horse carried you to us? In that profane train of mule-
teers you came with."

" You will judge, sir." It was like speaking to Saint
Michael of angels, speaking to Don Vito Cantú of
horses. "I ride a mahogany bay five years old. He is by
a gray they call Ruzio. Out of one of the old Toluca
Dulce mares."

"Which one?"

"One called Tsintsin."

"White hairs of a welted scar on her left shoulder.
A nearly black bay, tender-mouthed, and a natural
pacer."

"You know each one!" I said. Tsintsin was not a
notable mare.

"I remember each one," Don Vito Cantú said.
"Enough now, Master Toribio. De Ibarra. Tomorrow
in the dawn you saddle the mahogany pony. Have
your needments ready to travel. At the stone stable,
the one beyond the commissary. Tomorrow in the evening, if Indians have not eaten us meantime, you shall
see more Ibarra horses at a place I call Acuichál."

So dismissed I left him. My thought did not.

[13]

I lingered outside the *caja* to admire the disciplined comport of the stout old gray stallion standing with arched neck not far from the door. I studied the saddle of Don Vito Cantú. I had never seen one quite like it.

The head of the forebow was a curious round knob, big as an apple. Tied on the off side of this novelty was a coiled rope not of any ordinary fiber but of cunningly plaited rawhide, and it was noosed at one end. Low on the near side of the forebow hung something more familiar to me, though I had seen few, a leatherholstered big and wicked wheellock firearm of a military kind called *pistola de arzón*. The cantle forming the back of the fleece-padded sheepskin seat was lower and more rounded than a war saddle's. Lashed behind it were neither Spanish cloak nor saddlebags; only a folded and rolled blanket of the rough sort woven by Indians, and a thong-strapped gourd water bottle.

I spent the remainder of that day in impatience and loneliness of mind.

There are two blended sounds component to the workings of great mines like those of San Martín. One is the unceasing grind of stones turning in the crushers, cracking ore. The other is the unceasing rumble of hooves, hundreds of hooves, circuiting stone-flagged patio floors, pounding ore-mud with copperas and

Toribio

quicksilver, accreting amalgam of precious metal. There is a mournful murmur in the blended grind and rumble; and a smell of Lucifer accompanies the sound, in smoke and fire of furnace beds where raw billets of amalgam are so purged and roasted and steamed of dross that molten metal comes pouring at last into bars weighing thirty full marks of fine silver.

This pervading sound and acrid smell of wealth being born, these toils of wealth's midwives who like cunning Vulcan in his leather apron wrest the gleam of metal from dull rock, have not been matters of much appeal to my mind; though I admit a natural and inborn desire, which all have, to acquire a quantity of the final product of miners' toils, stamped from those bars of precious metal at the Mint. I know that by the Royal Fifth from the mines of our New Spain such bars made our Sacred Cesarean Catholic Majesty the richest king of earth. I know that such bars made my patron and protector, Don Diego de Ibarra, one of the richest lords of the Indies.

Yet I thought not of the great Ibarra mines but of the great Ibarra horses, while the hours turned toward the morrow.

We left the bleak porphyry cañon of San Martín in cold and windy earliest light.

There were only three of us, Don Vito Cantú, El Curaca Rivas, and I. With us came seven loaded pack-mules expertly handled by El Curaca, who was, I learned, Don Vito Cantú's chief herdsman and right-hand henchman; he had accompanied his master to San Martín, delivering horses and beeves for use at the mines. El Curaca in the idiom signifies "the boss" and it was his nickname. He was half Indian, from Compostela, and genial toward me as a stranger in the North and perhaps because my name was Ibarra.

Over a ridge and down the sandy stream bed of a wild ravine we came to the floor of a plain and rode out upon a limitless savanna of winter-yellowed tall grass.

I felt curiously remote from all I had known, and curiously elated as we turned north, riding into an

empty land enormous beyond all chart or measure.
After thirty-eight plodding days with a *conducta* of
packsaddled cranky mules all the way from the Valley
of Mexico, it seemed as if I entered that morning into
some legend of imagination, like a feat of Amadis of
Gaul or Prince Palmerin. The character of legend assumed the stamp of fact when El Curaca informed me
that the gray stallion ridden with such austere grace by
Don Vito Cantú was none other than the venerable
Gran Tordo, last war-horse of the conqueror of the
North, Don Francisco.

Even the pack animals seemed to gather the aura of
legend. One of them was loaded with all my clothes
and all my possessions including cuirass and morion.
The other half dozen carried what El Curaca called
treasures for Acuichál, all brought by the *conducta* and
traded at the mines for Acuichál beeves and horses: hard
brown cones of cane sugar, cacao beans and tropic
spices for making the sweetly frothed *chocolatl* bever-
age, tobacco leaves in bundles for medicinal smoking
tubes, cutlery including lance points, ax heads and an
adze, sauce plates and pewter cups, gunpowder and pig
lead, horseshoes and nails, salt, wool cards, garden
seeds, ells of brightly dyed serge and some fine cam-
bric, trinkets and herbs for women, two kilderkins of
authentic and powerful Jérez brandy. El Curaca rode

watching with an eagle's eye for any shift in the trim of such rare and precious ladings.

I rode hoping with a great silent earnestness that my own equestrian performance, the schooled correctness of my seat, the mode of my high and light hand, the propriety my horse evinced in carriage of head and action of leg, might be somewhat worthy of a Prince Palmerin's retinue — and at least tolerable in the eyes of Don Vito Cantú.

Though I knew he watched me, he rode without much speaking, seemingly withdrawn far into his own thought and an abstractness of mind. I was careful not to put myself forward.

It was after midday when he offered me a drink from the gourd water bottle, took one himself, and indicated an easier humor.

I shall not forget what he said to me as I rode with what I considered great seemliness at his distinguished side. "Toribio," said he, "a good horseman ought to show his mark by his ease with his task." He smiled. "Look, for example, at El Curaca Rivas persuading those mules as he rides through the high grass all day long to Acuichál. Note his long stirrups, how he sits with that rustic snubbing post of a saddletree and goes so easily in that limber country style without tiring himself or his horse. Then — you should see him when

more is required! That fellow is able and ready to catch an uncaught outlaw bull no matter if he must ride up to get him where the North Star burns his nose! And casting the *lazo!* He makes his horsemanship suit the occasion. It is possible, of course, to display here the *a la jineta* or even the *a la brida* riding figures taught us by gentlemen courtiers and tournament soldiers. Alas, we are a long way from palaces. Over that hill we might suddenly face the necessity of firing a pistol, wielding a sword or flipping a *lazo* around an Indian's evil throat. As you will see, here in the North we begin to neglect pomps. For convenience we become mere centaurs."

The sun was down to less than a hand's breadth above the earth and we were riding over the grassy shoulder of a long rise when a spacious valley opened to our view ahead and I saw in the distance small marks of humankind in the unmarked wilderness. Don Vito Cantú reined and turned to me, saying, "Under the little hill you see Acuichál."

It was the hour when the herds were brought in from their day's pasturing, to be enclosed for the night within the guarded shelter of walls. Distant files of slim-limbed horses and blockier shapes of slower cattle moved converging in the far quiet, raising thin pennons of golden dust above the golden grass in the golden light of day's end. A sense of legend and enchantment which I had felt earlier that day returned.

I suspect that some similar sense touched into the mind of Don Vito Cantú; he checked the gray stallion to a halt. "In Spain," he said, "the hamlet of my fathers has the name Dehesa de Oro. Where I was born. Pasture of Gold they called it, where they grazed the mare bands. They should see this one, this Ocean Sea of grass. This yet unfenced pasture with more nourishment for livestock than a half dozen complete Andalusias put together."

In the last finger of sunlight I caught the glint of the waterpond at the earthen dam by poplars and spring-greened brighter willows. Then there was only shade across the world. We rode on. My eyes found the plain square walls of a main house beyond trees, outbuildings and lean-to sheds, a round granary, the huddle and tangle of grass-thatched huts, the lanes and pens and great corral of dry-laid rock walling, all close under the hill's slope as if they were backed to it for protection in the barbarous space of the wilderness. I saw upon the hillside the positions of the pair of loop-holed stone blockhouses.

"It has not much grace," Don Vito Cantú said. "Not yet."

He gazed with an evident satisfaction across the

newly fenced and plowed and planted fields below the dam. "Seven years ago there was nothing. A cold spring by trees at the foot of a hill. Called by the Indians, Acuichál."

"Don Vito," I nerved myself to ask, "are the Indians still great peril and trouble here?"

"In general, no. In this district we see them baptized and more or less reduced. You saw some tamed ones at the mines. We have some better ones here; they performed the labor of our dam and all these walls. In those sierras to the northwest — " he pointed — "enough brute heathen Indians live with Satan for a master! And in the remote North past Santa Bárbola there are wild ones beyond numbering! And not yet known."

"Before we got to Zacatecas with the *conducta*," I said, "outlaw Chichimecs stole some of our mules. I was told they steal mules to eat. Do any raiders take livestock here?"

"Not lately! But it occurs, God knows it. Let me say, Master Toribio, and let yourself remember, there is a matter of very grave importance on this frontier: to keep all savages on foot! One of the first acts of the Marquis of the Valley, after he had won Mexico, was to issue the law prohibiting Indians from the use of the horse. Indians are strong, sometimes brave and very

cunning. Imagine them in all their numbers armed
with horses, making war on us, a few Christians, and
able to attack us and run from us horseback with their
arrows! I do not underestimate it. We take vigilant
pains to see that our horses serve only authorized persons, but this is thorny business, with such great increase of horse stock now and by no means enough of
Spaniards to control it. Or to tend cattle, for that matter. At Acuichál I grant the impossibility of herding all
cattle into pens at night. Some stray, some hide, some
vanish, the prey of wild beasts — and of wild Indians, it may be. However. We will keep our horses in
hand at all times! We will if there is any wisdom in us.
One thing is quite certain: from the day of Creation,
all this grass only waited to nourish great herds of
horses, and kine."

The air around us was alive with the sound and the
presence of stately cattle at water in peaceful twilight.
Past the dam we entered a rock-fenced lane that led to
the open yard in front of the main house. Two pic-
turesque riders saluted the master of Acuichál, baring
their heads as we passed; then they rode on, following
the stragglers of a horse herd through the opened gate
of a high-walled enclosure. Neck bells clattered. I
peered inside the gate, but with the movement and dust
in the dim light I saw little.

"Tomorrow you can fill your eyes," Don Vito Cantú said. " — If you like, you will even see the old mare Encanta. She and I — we are now the only two who have survived. Both of us came from the Serranía de Ronda. On the same leaky boat!"

El Curaca took our horses when we dismounted. A big and rough-coated type of staghound that did not bark came snuffing at our legs. "Good evening, Chasco," his master said.

Then I stepped from the gloaming into a room with a long table and hewn benches, lit with the amber glow of tallow dips, under the rooftree of Don Vito Cantú.

A young Indian woman, plump and pretty in a plain Spanish dress, came carrying an infant into the room. Behind her scurried two little girls in long muslin frocks, all to greet Don Vito. "My wife and babies," he said to me.

I bowed to them.

"This is Toribio, from Mexico," Don Vito said to them. "And he will live in this house."

Iba-rra

The remarkable Captain Hernán Cortés with his soldiery put the first horses upon the mainland of this New World. These horses, unlike their riders, came not from Spain. They were brought from Indies islands, mainly from the Española and Cuba, where colonizing Spaniards had been breeding horse stock for more than twenty years following the successful landing — by the Admiral Don Cristóbal Colón himself, on his second voyage — of the first brood mares and stallions ever in the Indies.

During the decades following the initial introduction of horses in New Spain, only a few horses arrived here directly from the Old World. There were good reasons. A sufficient seed stock was available in the Indies; at the same time there was a serious depletion and shortage of horses in Spain itself, owing to wars and other causes there. Moreover, a crossing from Europe in a tiny vessel on a tossing sea greatly increased the hazard, difficulty and expense of importation in comparison to a shorter, easier haul from Carib islands to the port of Vera Cruz. The few horses shipped across the breadth of the Ocean Sea had to be deemed special enough to justify the increase of trouble, risk and expenditure involved. Of those few, none that have been landed in our New Spain have evinced a more remarkable merit and value as prepotent seed stock than the splendid animals selected and brought directly from Spain, on the order and with the purse of the Knight Commander Don Diego, by Don Vito Cantú.

As a servitor and as a pupil granted certain privileges in the household of Don Diego I had spent a part of each year in the Valley of Toluca at one of the Ibarra *encomiendas* called Toluca Dulce. It was here that Don Vito Cantú was given all requisites to found and develop the Ibarra stud, using as its foundation stock two Berber stallions and five mares of Ronda-Valenzuela blood that had survived with Don Vito Cantú their stormy sea voyage from Cádiz.

Within the several subsequent generations of horses, Don Vito Cantú by his sagacity as a breeder, indeed by his genius, created and gave fixed character to a notable type and cast of horse which became known as the Ibarra, coveted by the most knowledgeable horsemen and the most active campaign soldiers of His Majesty's service in New Spain.

One of the first to recognize and to proclaim the merit of the Ibarra was that eloquent knower and rider of noble horses, our equestrian viceroy Don Luis de Velasco. His viceregal stables included several Ibarra horses (gifts of Don Diego) and it is a fact that he seldom rode any but these; they were not only of beautiful lineament and spirit, they were consummately retrained by "the hands of Cantú," as the lord Don Luis would declare often, explaining and demonstrating such training to the assembled company of his companions on horseback.

A dozen years after the establishment of the stud at Toluca Dulce, a great part of the soundest stock, both horses and mares, was transferred to the remote North, still in the charge of Don Vito Cantú, for the severe uses of Don Francisco and his cavalry in their exploration and conquest of the Nueva Vizcaya wilderness.

The Ibarras which in my boyhood I saw and rode and loved at Toluca Dulce were mainly the get of those horses retained by Don Diego near the capital and the viceroyalty for show, parade, formal equitation, bullfight fetes, cane games, polite riding, and as very useful gifts to important persons. The Toluca Ibarras were handled and tended by stable grooms under the supervision of an elegantly mannered Spanish riding master who was — though a well-born gentleman and my own instructor — in no category to be compared even dimly with such a figure as Don Vito Cantú.

The Acuichál Ibarras were mainly descendants of the veteran war-horses and brood mares that had been pastured at Don Francisco's own primitive *encomienda* he called Guatimape, in a mountain valley of Nueva Vizcaya's frontier. After his death most of this horse herd had been driven to another primitive range forty leagues distant: the pastures of Acuichál.

Now at this wilderness stud in the bright air of a springtime morning I began to see more exactly the measure and character of the true Ibarra horse straight from "the hands of Cantú."

In height, which was nearly always under fifteen hands; in weight, which was proportionate and not heavy; in head, which was broad of cheek and narrow of muzzle; in neck, which was thick and well set on fitly sloped shoulder; in back, which was short, with hip long; in musculature, which was robustly evident; in leg, which was stocky but cleanly shaped and with pastern well angled; in gait, which was springy and smooth; in action, which by nature was lively; in color, which could vary so much between individuals that no single color was called standard or even most common; in all these marks and traits, and in blood, the Ibarra was a strain of the Spanish-Barbary light saddle horse which the first conquerors brought to Vera Cruz.

To the discerning horseman's eye, Don Vito Cantú had bred and fixed a superior strain.

The Ibarra matured desirably a little broader of chest, noticeably deeper through the heart and at the back ribs, slightly wider through the hips, than the typical Spanish-Barbary saddle horse. The additional "room inside" and the increased compaction of body structure outside gave the Ibarra more stamina as well as greater force.

In the shape of the quarter and in the angle of the pelvis there was a most apparent point of difference between the Ibarra and his less distinguished blood brothers. In the Ibarra the drooped pelvis, or "goose rump," common to Spanish-Barbary stock was not seen. Instead, a profile view showed the more horizontal pelvic build which endowed the Ibarra with that full and unsloped croup and high set tail said to be characteristic of the Araby Kehilan Ajuz — though of course I have not seen an example of the ancient and revered breed.

Thus formed, displaying this powerfully framed quarter built to a good broad gaskin with the point of the hock well under the horse, the Ibarra possessed to an exceptional degree that quality called "collected-

ness" in action. Properly trained, it had no equal at plunging quick away from a standstill, or at veering sharp in a turn or a complete whirlaround nimbly controlled, or at avoidance of awkward "spreading" in headlong gallop, or at speediest changing or checking of pace. This was a saddle horse built and spirited to show keenest response with surest footing in fleetest requirement: and such was the merit of the exemplary Ibarra.

Between it and its brother, the Spanish-Barbary, there was another point of difference apparent even to those persons who unfortunately went afoot. The ram-like convex nose so characteristic of the Spanish-Barbary occurred rarely on the developed Ibarra head, being replaced by a straight but not dish-faced profile. Horsemen might call this less a matter of equine quality than of aesthetics.

As to the colors of the Ibarra: there were bays and browns of all hues; many dapple grays; duns with black mane and tail, linebacked, and usually with black points. Mouse grays, roans and piebalds occurred but were uncommon. Strangely, the strain produced few chestnuts; fewer yet of the true black called *hito*, and a pure white was not seen.

I found the frequency of the dapple gray, especially among the horses at Acuichál, worthy of notice. Dapple was often seen in the duns, giving their gold a rich splendor. A subtle dappling sometimes lived in the darker sheen of the bays, browns and chestnuts.

I remarked upon it, in the company of Don Vito Cantú.

"The better of the two stallions which I brought to New Spain," Don Vito told me, "was a dark dapple gray. You have admired one of his grandsons somewhat like him, the Gran Tordo I usually ride to San Martín. But the grandfather horse that crossed the sea with me — "

"Campeador?" I wanted him to know what I knew.

"Campeador. He was indeed." Don Vito's eyes went narrow musing through the corridor of the years. "The Champion. He had sailed once before. He was foaled not in the Serranía de Ronda, but in Africa."

This I did not know and he knew it.

"I have seldom recounted it," he said to me. "There were, at the time, excellent reasons for silence." The sharp points of Don Vito's mustachios moved slightly when he smiled. "I bought Campeador from a 'horse dealer' who said he was from Tangier. I think not. I saw the five-year-old stud at night, near Málaga, where that 'dealer' and a friend of mine had arranged to bring the horse. By a flickering light of torches I saw Campeador. I bought him there without trying him. At a considerable connivance. With a grave number of heavy golden *castellanos* poured from Don Diego's purse. Alone I rode the stallion to Ronda. In the dark. Then Cádiz. Where with fortune attending me I was able to find port officials ungraced with knowledge of horse-flesh. So the Campeador voyaged, with others less dis-tinguished, across the sea. He possessed, as no other horse I have known, ability to transmit to his offspring, male and female, the seed of his own quality. Time has proven it. And he was indeed what his seller claimed, of a great and pure blood from the Osmanli East. It was the Campeador who stamped these Ibarra dapples. It was he who gave these good ponies their Araby croups and deep hearts and straight-nosed faces. It was that potent-stoned singular horse, the stallion I bought at night without trying him, that brought whatever ac-complishment might be claimed for me as a stud mas-ter. Reflecting upon this, I have thought that to breed a noble horse is to share with God in one of His mys-teries. As well as one of His delights."

During those halcyon first days at Acuichál when all there was new to me, I found no entrancement greater than the study of the remarkable work I saw performed in a stable lot and upon a level plot of ground situated above the dam where young horses were gentled to the saddle and taught the lightest and finest of reining.

It was an equine academy without equal, maintained in a rough wilderness by a few skilled and trusted persons at the hands of Cantú.

Selected colts and fillies commenced to receive their training in the second year of their age, when these immature animals were brought in to stable for daily handling in order to accustom them agreeably to the presence and company of men.

To this end the young horses were rubbed down and curried once or twice a day, with much intermittent passage of persons in the enclosure, and pattings and attention given, and cuttings of hay hand-fed, and a little of corn, so that the animals felt never alone.

After a continued time of this first gentling, there was added to the rubbing and currying a daily bath, which was a sponging down of the animal's face and entire body, at a water trough especially for this purpose in the stable lot. It was done without splashing or any heavy hand to cause uneasiness and was followed invariably by a soothing, drying rubdown, to the top of the hooves. By such repeated daily handling and plenty of good feed the young horse was given growing assurance in the human voice and confidence in the benignity of the human hand. And for control at the time of the sponge-downs, a plain stable halter was introduced to the animal's head; in becoming accustomed to it, with little teaching the animal acquired complaisance with the act of being halter-led.

When so conditioned, upon another day immediately following bath and rubdown, the horse was introduced to the feel of a saddle upon the back for the first time.

It was usually accepted with little disquiet; but if the humor of the colt was judged very buoyant and spirited, a blindfold was applied with due care while the saddle was put into place. And by no means was the cinch band ever much tightened at this first saddling, for — have no doubt of it — the unfamiliar pressure, too abruptly applied, caused distress and distrust and destroyed previous gentling.

Loosely saddled, as I have said, the equine pupil was restrained and led by halter for a brief while in the training lot. The neophyte was led thus to perceive that no harm came from the strangeness and this was the lesson taught that day. On following days the saddle's cinching was brought gradually tighter, until the animal could accept without excitement a cinch tightened enough for a man to be able to mount into the saddle.

The right training of a colt will ever consist of an increasing routine performed daily, skipping no day whatsoever, for best result. Any horseman worthy of the name of *domador*, or tamer, must agree: the aim and object of his requiting labor is not to "break" a good horse but to make one.

At Acuichál, upon the day when a colt at length was ready to support a man in a cinched saddle, the ordinary stable halter was replaced by a training headstall equipped with a noseband and rope rein which I shall soon describe. Standing calm, accoutered with saddle and fitted headstall, the colt was then tail-roped to a most gentle and trained "godmother" mare brought in to stand by for this purpose. With the colt secured thus and while a groom held the colt's head, the *domador* with rope rein in hand stepped up into the saddle.

The measure of all the previous training was made manifest at that moment. While the colt responded according to its nature to rid itself of its first phlegm, then choler, the tail-rope attached to the placid godmother mare served to restrict and to quiet the young animal's actions. The *domador* sat clamped to the saddle, his right hand gripping the pommel. His feet pressed strongly in the stirrups, with his heels careful not to molest the animal's flanks, and his left hand held the rope rein. This was not jerked nor roughly pulled, but grasped with steady tension indicating to the animal the amenable carriage of its head.

In this manner the colt received its first instruction from a rider, each day for three consecutive days, and only briefly. For the purpose of the lesson was to train, not to tire the colt, or to plant dread or revolt in it. After the third day the colt was neck-roped rather than tail-roped to the restraints of the godmother. After three more days, she was dispensed with. Then the man in the saddle began to ride the colt unaccompanied, controlling and instructing it by means of the training halter's rope rein.

No bitted bridle was employed.

[41]

The young horse at Acuichál did not feel the heavy rigor of levering metal on tongue or palate or jaw un-til *after* rein-training was already well accomplished; and I record this as another attribute of the genius that dwelt in Don Vito Cantú.

For I state the truth, which some may doubt, when I say these best-bitted mounts in New Spain acquired their discipline of the reins not by a curb of iron in the mouth but by a mere knot of horsehair under the chin.

Their remarkable discipline was imparted by means of a remarkable training halter which we call the *já-quima*, created by Cantú.

In actuality it was the cunning refinement and de-velopment of the Spanish horse trainers' traditional headstall called *cabezón de la brida,* a cavesson with a stiff noseband, conventionally used with and in addi-tion to a bitted bridle during a horse's first subjugation under saddle. As perfected by Cantú, this cavesson be-came the much lighter and more effective *jáquima;* and he used it without any bridle. New Spain's good horse-men will learn the virtue of it: simple yet subtle, mild yet mighty, in the making of a horse finely mouthed.

Don Vito's *jáquima* consisted of two strings' of plain whang leather which were tied to fit over the poll and positioned down both cheeks properly to hold in place a hard noseband of roundly plaited rawhide.

´D O M A D O R

Then came the essential business of the matter. Securely tied to the back of the noseband, where the tapered rawhide shanks met for a heel knot centered under the horse's chin, was a strong and prickly horsehair rope (tail hairs were coarser than hair from the mane; cowtail hair was coarsest of all) usually seven *varas* in length. Hence, by bringing an ample loop of hair rope back and over the withers, then forward to run again fastened through the heel knot, reins were fashioned. And what remained of the seven *varas,* issuing from the tie at the heel knot, was long enough for a lead or tie rope when the rider dismounted leaving the rein still looped over the withers.

The efficacy of Cantú's *jáquima* did not reside in pressure it could apply by the hard rawhide band across the soft front cartilage of a horse's nose. This was only an adjunct to the action. The true secret of the *jáquima* depended upon something else, and this was a careful fitting of the heavy rough-haired heel knot to an adjusted position — hanging clear but with a most precise modicum of clearance — close beneath the sensitive and vulnerable spot which is under the equine chin; so that any pull back on the rein or any tightening shift of it pulling sideward raised the hair knot to chafing contact on the tender-fleshed spot under the chin.

[45]

Easing of the rein's pull brought instant relief. In a natural desire to remedy the knot's prickle, the horse reacted with a movement to ease the rein's tension. In such response the animal came to know by experience that a kind of counteraction was required for each signal from the rein, and when the counteraction was performed the chin's discomfort ceased.

As daily training progressed, the skillful trainer taught the horse to respond to the threat rather than to the actually applied pressure of the irritating knot.

If, for example, there came a gently lifting even pull on the reins, the horse discovered and remembered that to come to an instant halt was to avoid the vexation under the chin; for when the horse stood still the trainer would instantly slack the reins. By the same token, the irritant scratchiness of the hair-rope rein itself became as functional as the hair knot. In teaching the horse to obey the command to turn to the right or to the left, the trainer would be careful to bring the horse's head around not only by the sideward but by the downward pull of the rein: this *prevented* the knot from raising to contact under the chin, but *caused* the hairy prickle of the rein against the neck. So the signal for a turn became the touch of the hair-rope rein on the side of the neck, and that was all. By experience of this kind, repeated again and again daily, the horse's obedience to the rein became reflexive action; when the always light but always firm hand of the trainer had made it familiar enough, the horse performed it dependably enough.

The *jáquima's* hair knot and rope rein accomplished all the customary work of the bridle's iron bit — without any cruel metal to injure or deaden the pliant tractability of a horse's mouth in early training.

Each horse became accustomed to saddle and responsive to hair-rope reins at the hands of a *domador*. Four of these tamers, all sensible horsemen with good hands, regularly served at Acuichál. A *domador* could have a dozen horses in his charge at one time and he gave each of them exercise daily with the *jáquima*, not too much at a time, but enough, depending upon aptitude and circumstance.

When the horse was judged ready, from three to six months after it was first ridden — for some are better

and learn more easily than others — it was advanced
to training at the hands of another man known as an
arrendador, literally a "reiner." There were but three
men of such recognized standing at Acuichál: Don
Vito Cantú in charge of all, a broken-nosed Córdo-
ban named Guzman, and a wiry veteran known simply
as Old Lope. (His son, a good *domador*, was Young
Lope.)

The *arrendador* was the subtle master of equitation's
high art. He introduced a horse to the bitted bridle, the
leather reins' and the spurs' signals; under his tutorage
then a horse received highest schooling and final refinement of the rein. The *arrendador* might work with
as many as four animals daily and his teaching might be
continued, with the best mounts, for a twelvemonth or
more.

The first few times the bridle's curb was fitted in the
horse's mouth, it was the custom at Acuichál to sprinkle
some salt on the wetted bit, that the horse might be a
little pleasured.

The bridle by no means immediately replaced the
jáquima. During a transition period, both were used on
the horse's head at the same time. For the first three
days the bridle was put on for the sole purpose of ac-
quainting the horse with the hang and the feel of the
bit in the mouth. Nothing more. The bridle reins, held

in the right hand only, were not used in any way. Commands of the rein still issued entirely from the *jáquima's* rope rein held in the left hand.

Gradually and with mildness of touch the bridle rein was used concurrently with the rope rein, in such manner that the horse accepted the action of the bit in the mouth as a merely concomitant part of the rope rein's already familiar action. As the horse became seasoned with more training, the bridle rein's command substituted for that of the rope rein and finally replaced it. Then the bridle was worn alone. And the horse now controlled by the bit, yet never having suffered the punishment the iron could deal, came to the finishing phase of training with fine mouth and ready response to the lightest of hands.

With exact propriety the horse learned to turn leftward "asking for the rider," as we say, when the *arrendador* put foot into stirrup to mount. The horse learned to stand perfectly still when so commanded. It learned ready obedience to subtlest pressures of command in starts and halts, turns and whirls, backings, controlled and smoothly linked zigs and zags, instant pirouettes, abrupt changes of direction and pace, bursts and checks of speed from the walk, trot, canter. Top horses were taught a kind of quick curvet leap nobly gay for flourish; a splendid few were able to perform a

mode of advancing *levade* with iron-shod forefeet pawing air, to the terror of Indians afoot.

Elegancies of dancing parade and tournament training, formal evolutions and figures *de la jineta y brida*,
were unsuitable for the practical horsemanship of frontier explorers, campaign soldiers, couriers, travelers,
miners, wilderness stockmen. In the realities of the life
such horsemen led daily, the true necessity might be
the mount that could carry and aid rider in accurate
cast and catch of his *lazo;* the mount taught to stand
calm in firearms' din; the mount trained to sustain lancer
or long-swordsman in any raw tumult of action against
uncivilized and unmounted foemen; all of which is to
say — an amenable, sure-footed, untiring horse able to
carry a rider to ends of earth and bring him home, not
failing in faithfulness. These were requirements, and
this was doctrine at Acuichál, as I learned and as the
horses did also.

There the ultimate schooling of a saddle horse was
so consummate that I saw with my own eyes a powerful five-year-old stallion in marvelous amenity being
put through every change of gait and speed, every se-
verity of plunging start, quick check, sliding stop, sudden turn, twist, whirl, *levade*, curvet, in everything being commanded and controlled by reins resting with a
seeming feather lightness around the easy upturned

Arrendador

crooking of one finger of a left hand. These reins were
not conjoined, that day, by the customary clasp of a
braided leather *ramal* knot. They were fastened together
and held in the crook of the finger by a single strand
of horsehair plucked from the stallion's mane. The one
hair carried all the reins' commands.

Such were the hands of Cantú.

When he dismounted from this display, Don Vito
said to us, "Show me the dullard who rides with a
tight rein and I will show you his ruined horse. You
are sowing gapeseed, Master Toribio! There are
merely four attributes required of a horseman! But to
lack any one of them is to lack them all: perception,
judgment, light hand, patience indestructible."

A poplar tree cast a quiet
shade along one side of the training paddock's trodden
ground. Hoofmarks there in manifold printings and
patterns signed the signature of Acuichál: where noble
horses learned not only to serve the venturings but to
share the lives of men.

From the very beginning I had hoped Don Vito would assign me some labor on the training lot or at least require me to serve him as a groom in the young horses' stable yard. I was hard put, hiding my disappointment, when he gave me orders setting me to work as a cowherd! It seemed a great misfortune.

"El Curaca and his crew will keep you occupied," was all Don Vito said.

So each day at the sun's rising I saddled my horse Caobo, the mahogany bay, and we went out to the pastures tending the herds accordingly as we were commanded by El Curaca Rivas.

For the day's work I found myself paired usually with Joaquín Ripalda, in whose company I quickly learned what a green novice I was and how I needed seasoning of a kind I had not encountered riding the

Joaquín Ripalda

cobbles of Coyoacán or the confines of Toluca Dulce
or even the mule path to Nueva Vizcaya.

Ripalda was an indentured Spanish Vizcayan origi-
nally from Hergueta, a burly man of forty years' age,
formerly an Ibarra trooper, swarthy, bearded, and of
great strength. I freely afforded him my youthful respect; while he accorded me, or the position he imagined I had, a courteous but far from servile deference.

The years had made him a most authentic leather-
clad denizen of the New World's untrammeled Vizcaya. He showed me, brusquely when I deserved it,
how to perform El Curaca's specific orders in the driving, drifting, grazing, watering, gathering, watching
and finding of livestock on unfenced and unprotected
pastures. Ripalda's own performance appeared flaw-
less to me; watching his ease with his task, I found it
nearly necessary to conclude that he actually knew
what the huffish bull or simpleton heifer or skittish
horse would do next because he knew what it would
be *thinking* next. Whether or not Joaquín Ripalda was
able to give thought in the mode of dumb beasts, he
handled their vagaries by some wile that did command
them; for he owned that rustic sapience, or great store
of useful lore, which a mindful man acquires living
close to the secrecies of the mother earth.

During long days in quiet while cattle fed and time

passed slowly, he imbued my mind with some share of his own active and sharp-eyed familiarity with the marks and shapes, the characters and features, of the outstretching pastures. I learned from him their watering places and their limits, their grasses and browses, which were choicest and where they grew best, the signs of weather in the sky, the tracks of beasts on the earth.

Gazing at the cow brutes in our charge, he was fond of using a country word, *vaquero*, to describe our work. He used it with pride, like a badge, describing himself. "I am *vaquero*," he would say, as if it explained all. "Not *caballero*, God knows it — " he would glance mildly at me — "but *vaquero. Vaquero* of the North, where the cows grow."

As any *vaquero* must, I began to learn the use of the *lazo*.

Ripalda was expert, afoot or from horseback. He required me first to acquaint my hands well with the heft and feel of the plaited rawhide rope itself, its pliancy yet its stiffness, the inbuilt twist of its plait, the turn and spring of its coiling; and exactly how the *lazo*, literally the snare, ought to be disposed in the right hand with the coiled length of the rope ready in the left, initial to its use.

Then he showed me the five phases of a good cast:

the preliminary spreading of the noose's opened loop, the whirling about of the loop overhead while aiming, the throw releasing the open loop forward in the momentum of its whirl, the pull back or the flip to close the noose, and the brace or snub to take the jolt of the catch.

To be shown rightly was one thing. To emulate rightly was another.

The trick was compassed by dint of much practice at every offering target, be it wooden post or milk calf. The throw itself could be perfected only by dint of experience, afoot first, in and out of a stock pen, then in the saddle, at all speeds; and each man's arm, wrist, hand and eye will find its own style and form its own habit in acquiring the knack.

Manipulation of the rawhide loop was frustration first, then fascination, then obsession, and finally not only a great utility but a pastime most delectable. I found it thus. So did my Toluca bay, Caobo, for it is truth to say that a horse of Ibarra blood seemed to know by instinct and predilection what was required when the flank was touched and the rawhide sang overhead.

To cast a *lazo* from horseback was of course a folly and an evident danger if the saddle provided no convenient means of securing the end of a rope after a catch was made. The design of a saddle with this ac-

commodation, this necessity, was an inherent and con-
current part of the invention of a *lazo*. The one was
useless without the other: to go armed with a rope
meant also to ride a saddle with a pommel shaped and
reinforced to serve as a snubbing post for the rope in
action. Such a pommel was devised by building into
the peak of the saddle fork a stout hardwood ball-
shaped knob, called the apple. A deft turn of the rope
around the base of the apple could snub up and belay,
adjustably, the *lazo's* catch. In case of mischance, re-
lease of the turn could free the rope if necessary. It was
not tied on.

A lame old sergeant horseman with the name of
Gonzalo Duro served at Acuichál as artificer of saddletrees and headstalls. He lived and worked in a little
room by the smithy, and Ripalda and he were cronies.
The sergeant, in exchange for the brass-studded city
saddle I had ridden from Coyoacán, and after some
negotiation, provided me with a plain but sturdy rop-
er's saddle such as I very greatly desired. It was much
like Don Vito's.

Old Duro's room smelled of leather and wood chips,
wild beeswax and green rawhide. I liked to go there.
Aproned at his bench, within the sound of hooves and
the nearby farrier's hammer, Duro was at times full of
remembrance, and of his own kind of eloquence.

"In those days there in the Valley of Mexico," the old sergeant said, "we lived very happy with him, that viceroy Don Luis de Velasco. We called him Aquel Buen Caballero, meaning not so much Yonder Good Gentleman, but Yonder Good Horseman! We could have said Aquel Buen Jinete, but it did not seem enough. I tell you, he was no mere lord and master living exalted in the principal house.

"Each Saturday it was his custom to leave the cares of his state and mount a flash-reined son of the stallion Campeador and ride out to Chapultepec, which was the forest in back of his dwelling, beyond town, where he ordinarily kept at last a half dozen savage bulls to run, and where he had built good stone bullpens and a pretty enclosure for sport.

"He went out there accompanied by the most prominent personages of the city, perhaps a hundred men horseback, with their grooms and servants. Every Saturday!

"We all would deck our horses with breastbands of hawk bells and ride in the music.

"This rare viceroy himself would lead us in all sport. We would match race the best horses in New Spain, play the rousing game of hurling the canes, and then prove our lances and manhood against those wild bulls. The viceroy not only led it, but excelled!

[61]

"We felt true delight at being the horseback companions of such a compatible and excellent man. We rejoiced in pleasing him, we honored ourselves by his company.

"You should have seen Vito Cantú in the saddle, those days. Those knock-pate games with a viceroy. Angels Custodian! You should have watched those two on the horses of Don Diego de Ibarra.

"Each and every Saturday without fail, fine food and drink, largesse of Don Luis, was served to each and every horseman present. It was no light breaking of fast after exercise, but a banquet invariably, there under the trees and plentifully served on good plate.

"And so politic and gallant was this viceroy that when he would ride homeward and the streets where he rode would fill with horsemen, he would call out to a humble groom, or even a saddler sergeant, and ride galloping with him abreast, him only, in order that no envy might be stirred among the gentlemen horsemen for his riding with one and not another, and none could feel partiality.

"Concerning this saddle that we Ibarra people ride at Acuichál and that I make, it comes from those Saturdays at Chapultepec, and in this manner exactly:

"It so happened that a bull jumped a wall, escaping the pen. It so happened that those mounted men plying their *garrochas*, using those wooden poles in the ancient and customary Spanish manner of handling cattle, failed entirely to control the escaped bull and a man was gored.

"Then came a very courageous Indian servant afoot, armed with nothing but the clever rope snare he used in hunting. With a toss of the loop by sheerest fortune while he ran, this Indian snared the bull by both forefeet and tumbled it with a very neat jerk! Of course he could not hold, lacking the strength, or a snub. But the bull was chastened very much by the fall and, dragging the snare, was lured by the horsemen with the poles back into the trap and pen.

"Yonder Good Horseman Don Luis was enchanted with the brave Indian and his snare. He was moreover enchanted by a thought which came into his mind: the creation of a new equestrian utility, a new equestrian sport! Naturally, Don Luis lost little time conveying such a thought to the finest-handed horseman of our epoch. Who needs to name him? Then the Indian, they called him in, to examine the snare and learn the knack. A certain artisan of saddletrees was called in. He needs no naming. Does he?

"And you see it! From a Saturday afternoon at Chapultepec. Soon now every boy cowherd of New Spain will require one, and use one.

[63]

"Our friend Ripalda terms it a *vaquero* saddle. He seems to have no feel on his tongue for saying he works with cows in a viceroy's saddle.

"If any felt the need for a name of strict correctness, it would be necessary to call it what it is: a Cantú saddle.

"Yet we who make it with our own hands name it in our art now a Saddle of Don Luis de Velasco. Recalling those Saturdays, who would find fault with such a memorial?"

In evenings of springtime at Acuichál when supper was finished and the day's work done, sometimes I went walking. If my steps led me leftward from the main house, across the cart yard and down a walled lane, frequently I saw Gonzalo Duro seated on the bench outside his workroom, taking his ease an hour or so before bedtime. Joaquín Ripalda might be there visiting with his crony, or it might be the Old Lope or El Curaca, sharing a smoking tube of the black Querétaro *tabaco indio.*

Occasionally the veteran saddler sergeant would be sitting alone at his familyless door in the dark; at times I think he felt as lonely in his age as I felt lonely in my youth.

"Toribio de Ibarra," he greeted me one evening, and I saw he was alone and wanting company. "Sit down awhile. And tell me something."

"Command me," said I.

"Tell me this. Do you know that in feature and aspect you bear resemblance to the lamented Francisco de Ibarra?"

My surprise must have been evident. I answered by saying, "I did not know it. Nor did I ever see our Captain General, in life."

"Of course not. He was here in the North." I felt the old man's eyes peering at me in the dark. He said, "I recall him when he was your present age, and beardless. Others, like myself, must have mentioned to you the resemblance."

"None have," I said.

"Well — " He spoke the word as if it loosed his grasp of the matter. "Excuse me. My intention was complimentary."

"There is nothing to excuse," I said. "And I take it

[65]

as a compliment, being likened in any way to Don Francisco. Though he exists in my own mind more as legend, it may be, than as an actual man who walked earth."

"I'll warrant he was actual enough! Though I would say that he rode rather than walked the earth, whenever possible. And I with him, whenever possible! From the Valley of Mexico to the Valley of Guatimape — "

"You knew him when he was young as I am."

"Younger! The first time I ever saw him he was horseback in the company of his riding master Don Vito Cantú, who was teaching him the circlings *de la brida*. And next, at the garden of Don Diego's house in Coyoacán, I saw the boy with a teacher of assuredly different stripe, a very learned and very skinny friar — "

"Cienfuegos," I said.

"You knew him?"

"He taught me. In that same garden."

"Ha! Everybody knew Cienfuegos. He preached to my troop, usually about Hell, on Sundays of Lent. Friar Hundred Fires. He looked very durable, though thin. Do the Hundred Fires burn yet, or are they gone to a Hundred Heavens?"

"Gone," I said. "Three summers past. He even

[66]

taught me some Latin! And it is necessary to admit that he was a good teacher. Strict, but good."

"It must have struck old Hundred Fires. I mean to say, how you resembled his earlier pupil."

"He never mentioned anything of that kind."

"Didn't he ever speak of Don Francisco?"

"Most certainly he did! But in a lofty style always. Almost as lofty as the Invincible Cavalier Don Polindo."

"Eh?"

"In such words as these, which he would have me memorize and then commit, letter by letter, into my copy book, to show Don Diego: 'He grew to manhood as an accomplished grammarian, as a heroic horseman, as an ardent Christian; so endowed, he became a noble captain, an intrepid discoverer, an equitable governor of New Lands.' "

"Phew," the sergeant said. "That's Don Polindo?"

"It's Don Francisco," I said. "According to the Friar Cienfuegos."

"Well. Up here in the North I would not be certain that grammar was of great aid. It seems unlikely. Being an ardent Christian would help more, usually, though it occurs to me that an excessive Christian may experience an occasional disadvantage. As to the horsemanship which the friar mentioned, it was not only of

greatest help, it was of greatest necessity! However.
This Gonzalo Duro now makes saddletrees and plaits
jáquimas. He sits in no judgment concerning endow-
ments of captains, discoverers or governors."

"Tell me something, if you will, Gonzalo Duro."

"Command me." I could see that he grinned.

"When you first came to the North, what year
was it?"

"Let's see. I was at Zacatecas first, it was the year
'54. But we went back to the Valley of Mexico to re-
fit and remount the troop. One could say that I did
not become an authentic Northerner until '62."

"What makes one an authentic Northerner?"

"I consider that I became one gradually by never
again finding myself any farther south than the Bufa of
Guanajuato," Gonzalo Duro said. "As to the year of
1562, some of us are not apt to forget that date. This
remotest province of New Spain was founded. The
New Vizcaya. Bounded on the south by the New Ga-
licia. Bounded on the north by the edge of the whole
world! And whether this may be the Sea of Ireland or
coasts of Tartary Cipangu very close to the side of the
Terrestrial Paradise peopled by the dark women living
in the fashion of Amazons, none can say because none
have been there yet to see. Or, at least, none have returned to inform us here at Acuichál. In the midsum-

Gonzalo Duro

mer of the year '62 Don Francisco de Ibarra was in-
vested with royal authorization and formal appointment
as Governor and Captain General of Nueva Vizcaya.

"And we rode with him into the North beyond anything known, to subjugate hostile Indians and pros-
pect for mines.

"Few of us ever saw the South again. Many of us
were killed. Many of us died of ills, or of exertions.
Some of us the Indians ate. Some of us became knaves.
Or great scoundrels. Or fugitives. There were those
among us who became lamed veterans more or less disappointed and more or less disabled, except for the
wag of our tongues. And a few were heroes, I think,
though I have not seen any as formally heroic as those
occurring in books.

"From my point of vantage planted on this bench at
my age of sixty-nine, it appears to me that perhaps the
most successful of us who came North were the horses
wearing the Ibarra brand. They flourish most certainly,
as we do not."

"There is also," I answered him, "another handle
by which to lift the cup: 'Horses are of no account
without the men to ride them.'"

"Well spoken! Yet, when recollecting in candor, I
ponder how success so seldom accompanied those men
whose deeds I witnessed, and shared! Pardon me if I

[71]

take as an example the memory of one who had all qualities worthy of reverence:

"Five years ago this summer Don Francisco de Ibarra died not in the heat of battle, as he would have wished, but in the fever of a sickbed. He died not in ripeness of years and fullness of accomplishment but at the age of only thirty-six, when a man's achievement ought to be in its early and not its late fruition. He died not with any of the world's homage, which he deserved, but nearly alone in a rude house in rude wilderness, which he had conquered.

"He was aware of one kind of success, which was the recognition accorded him in the hearts of soldiers he led bravely and people he governed justly. This may well be success of the highest spiritual kind. But I do not believe for a moment that is all the success a great lord with great ambition and great ability would hope for. He was cut off before his work was done; before the measure of his success could arrive to reward him. He was cut off sorrowfully. We watched him weaken and waste with the coughing up of his life's blood, to die exhausted in the phthisis that consumed him.

"It was Old Lope and I who rode from Guatimape the twoscore leagues to the camp house here by the water of Acuichál, to tell Don Vito Cantú that our cap-

tain lay dying. And we got back in time: our captain
died with his hand resting in Don Vito's hands, and
with us to stand watch while the soul departed.

"In these five years the house and all else at Guatimape falls to ruin with no one of any caste there to tend
it well, with the horses all gone, with the cattle stolen or
running unbranded and wild as deer in the mountains.
As if Don Francisco de Ibarra had not lived. Except,
for a few of us, here — " Gonzalo Duro's dark hand
tapped at the location of his own heart.

I was impelled to attempt some reply. I said, "The
horses do bear the Ibarra name."

For a livestock brand at
Acuichál, Don Vito Cantú used no mark of his own.
He branded only the famed sign and device of the
Ibarra family, the Cross-Enflanked I; this would be
continued, I understood, until perfected cadastral title
to Acuichál was achieved, at which time a tally and final settlement of the livestock property, both horses

and cattle, would by agreement be made between Don Vito Cantú and his patron Don Diego de Ibarra.

I had lived all my life with the Cross-Enflanked I in evidence about me, written on paper, impressed in wax, carved in wood, embroidered in silk, stamped in silver, woven in wool, graved in die metal, tooled in leather, wrought in iron. Now I helped burn it on the living hides of beasts.

At calf-branding time all horsemen, young and old, joined in the work of gathering, holding and handling the herds. Solemn wielders of red-glowing stamp irons moved in the midst of great bawlings of cattle, shouts of ropers, throwers, wrestlers of calves, smells of dust, woodsmoke and much burnt hair. There was good humor in sharing the task and immense opportunity to use our *lazos*, though it must be admitted that most of the roping was performed by skilled senior horsemen, and to us less experienced fell the robustious and often comic toils with the kicking calves and their horned mothers.

It was Whitsuntide when the branding was done and we finished reshaping the herds for the summer's pasturing. Don Vito considered it fitting to mark the completion of the work by a festival day for Acuichál: by special invitation and arrangement the Father Gaspar Buendía, curate at the San Martín mines, upon Whitmonday rode a black mule and led a gray one, carrying vestments and all sacramental necessaries, the fifteen leagues to Acuichál.

For the first time ever, on Whit-Tuesday morning of that year 1580, Acuichál heard a church bell and a blessing intoned, consecrating a chapel site and a plot of ground for a cemetery sanctified by sign of Cross, and water of Life. The visiting father heard confessions, granted absolutions, celebrated the Mass, administered the sacraments of matrimony and of baptism for which numbers stood gravely in need. Father Buendía generously dispensed Christian blessings that day and at length joined Don Vito his host, whose children were among those baptized, at the long table set up in front of the main house where there were feasting and dancing to music of pipe, tabor and Ronda guitar of five strings.

The cleric was no dour Franciscan; both he and the master of Acuichál were Andalusians, from villages not six leagues apart. They freely quaffed brandy from the Jérez cask.

That evening the *arrendador* Old Lope came to the long table to whisper in Don Vito's ear. He brought word that the mare Encanta, last survivor of the voyage from Cádiz, had fallen dead. I believe that it affected Don Vito, stirring recollections which had long rested in the past.

When we returned from the stall where the aged mare lay stilled, many of us sat awhile again at the long table lit now by bonfires under the stars. I, for one, listened rapt to Don Vito Cantú as he recalled to Father Buendía times before I was born.

The weakness of a tired horse, as Don Vito spoke of it that night, assumed power to shape history. New Spain had numerous examples of tired horses not to be forgotten, he said.

For instance, the fall of a tired horse killed by inglorious accident the glorious Pedro de Alvarado, after a thousand battles. The fall of a tired horse struck the doughty Vásquez de Coronado such a clap on the skull as to addle his mind and cause him to forsake search of the golden Quivira, after a thousand leagues. The fall of a tired horse crippled the Knight Commander Don Diego de Ibarra for the rest of his long life and incidentally brought us here to Acuichál, after a thousand pains.

This fall of the tired horse, this accident on the fierce mountainside trail from the Zacatecas mines, which he had discovered, one bitter night in the year 1549 so injured and lamed the spine of Diego de Ibarra that he was never again able to mount and ride in a saddle.

The misfortune only temporarily daunted him.

The disability only temporarily cut him off from pursuit of his ambition.

As soon as he was able, he wrote a letter for delivery across the Ocean Sea. He addressed it to his elder brother, the Vizcayan hidalgo Don Pedro de Ibarra, Inquisitor of Toledo, widower, noble father of a noble son.

The letter contained two eloquent requests from the adventuring Diego in the New World:

One was to ship him horses that would not tire.

The other was to send into his care and devotion a young Ibarra who could tireless ride untiring horses, for the sake of great glory in Heaven and great riches on earth: conquering New Spain's unknown North for the Sacred Cesarean Royal Majesty.

Accompanying the letter was the additional eloquence of a heavy great chest, sealed and bonded with the viceroy's own signet to the care of the Casa de Contratación at Seville for delivery to the Inquisitor at Toledo. The chest contained nothing but lawfully licensed and enstamped thirty-mark bars of silver bullion, of a high *tepuzque* gold content, from Zacatecas. The Inquisitor possessed the talent to employ and to enjoy such bounty. It greatly aided him to attain an attitude favoring fulfillment of requests made by his brother in the Indies.

Concerning horses, Don Pedro de Ibarra sought the expert advice of equestrian friends at court. Concerning the possible future career of his twelve-year-old son Francisco, he consulted his own heart. Thereupon he set about the making of appropriate plans and arrangements.

These matters took a favorable turn in the late autumn of 1551 when Don Pedro interviewed a highly recommended young gentleman horseman, son of a modest hidalgo from the vicinity of Ronda, who had recently delivered splendidly bred and exceptionally trained Barbary saddle horses to the gallant Duke of Medina Sidonia. Don Pedro reposed his confidence in the newly met twenty-six-year-old *maestro de equitación,* and was not disappointed as time passed. As a buyer of horses and as a handler of funds from another man's purse, he proved to be as trustworthy as he was discerning — though in one instance he did seem to spend inordinately for a particular gray stallion. The knowledge he possessed in paddock and stable was matched by the skill he displayed in the saddle, both *de la jineta* and *de la brida.* Most importantly, he showed himself as an acceptable preceptor, guide and companion for the son of an Ibarra.

Hence, at Cádiz upon a gray morning half a year later the Inquisitor Don Pedro de Ibarra dismally but with comforts of Faith waved a farewell and watched the Indies Fleet galleon *Santangel de Sanlúcar* work wind and tide standing out to sea. She was bound for the excessively distant port La Villa Rica de la Vera Cruz in a new Spain. She carried away from an old Spain young Francisco de Ibarra and his teacher Evaristo Rodrigo Cantú with a dozen selected horses — five stallions, seven mares — from the Serranía de Ronda.

Their voyage required sixty-eight days at sea.

For humankind such voyaging was a hardship and a trial; for horses penned in plank stalls jerry-built on the open weather deck in the ship's waist, the only available space, such voyaging was torture.

Only at times of calm, occurring seldom, could the horses' benumbed legs feel any relief of firm stance in the cramped stalls. Most of the time, in order that they might not sprawl and fall, hurting themselves, each horse had to be suspended inside its confining stall by means of a sail-canvas sling, like a hammock, rigged under the belly and held up by lashings to a beam overhead.

In this frightening, unnatural and inescapable confinement which a horse could not be made to under-

stand, unprotected from weather in storm or mountainous seas or doldrum under tropic sun, a helpless horse
had to endure the cruelty of the heaving deck, or die.

Assisted by one inept apprentice seaman assigned to
him during certain watches, and by the boy Francisco,
who helped as he was able, Don Vito Cantú lived on
the open deck week after week with the weakening
horses, sharing their misery, providing them with such
care and such aid as he found in his power. He noted
that mares, possessed of female patience and stamina of
spirit for survival in adversity, generally coped with
continued attrition better than stallions. Of the five
studs embarked at Cádiz, three died at sea. Of the
seven mares, two were lost. Each time it became necessary to push one more wasted, pitiably bony dead body
over the side into the surge of the sea, Don Vito Cantú
wept.

On the forty-fifth day of her ocean crossing *Santan-*
gel de Sanlúcar made through the Indies' Windward
Passage. Four days later she spoke Sant' Jago, but did
not put in to the Buen Tiempo harbor for renewal of
fresh water stores there, owing to fears of villainous and
heretical English freebooters lurking for Spanish ships.
Providential squalls, almost daily during the following
week, brought some catchment of rainwater aboard the
storm-battered and sea-wearied galleon; running on,

she sailed the chopping seas of the channel past Cape Catoche to the Campeche Bay, where, with winds favoring and with her rotten pumps at work through all watches, she came finally to the roadstead's quietness at Vera Cruz.

The scarecrow horses were secured into their canvas slings for the last time. One by one they were hoisted outboard by the gun tackle, and eased down into a lighter. Then they were rowed to the beach. They managed to stand again upon the kindness of the firm, unmoving earth. They managed to drink again of sweet water, fresh and flowing. They managed to taste again a little newly cut hay. They had their first mouthfuls of the life-renewing, big-grained golden Indies corn.

In the ordeal of this transplantation from an old continent to a new, horses could not be subjected to more rigorous trial of mettle, or provide more poignant proof of endurance. Neither the faithless nor the feeble survived.

The seven survivors were as remarkable in their recovery as they had been in their endurance. Thirteen weeks after tottering ashore they were filled out in flesh, smooth of coat, lively of gait, and climbing the conquerors' trail up from the hot country to the temperate and inspiriting air of the high Valley of Mexico.

The mare Encanta, Don Vito said, was of the

[83]

strong Moorish Guzman blood, an untried filly two years old when she arrived, and the youngest of all that left Dehesa de Oro. She matured with a kind of sinewy grace which endowed her with great hardihood and a seeming power against age; during nearly twenty years of fertility she never dropped a weak or common foal!

The morning after her death, before Father Buendía set out again for San Martín he was drawn by Don Vito into certain discussion, not without warmth of word, concerning the Christian propriety of burying a beast, such as an old mare, in holy ground. Regardless, when the reverend father had departed from Acuichál, and was well beyond sight, a grave was dug in the newly blessed *campo santo* intended for remains of beings possessing souls. We laid the mare Encanta into that grave. Don Vito himself helped us cover her over, far from Ronda.

Then from the great North came an old soldier and a strange Indian to us at Acui-chál. They were not expected.

They came unseen, unannounced, unescorted by any watcher or herder from any of Acuichál's outlying pastures, in the gray evening of Saint John Baptist's Day, during a gray rain.

The soldier was riding a lamed blue roan horse the color of rain. The Indian was afoot driving a sore-footed string of burdened donkeys the color of rain. Gloaming and great space produced them out of noth-ingness, suddenly to appear in the far end of the walled yard at the house of Don Vito Cantú.

We jostled from the supper table, out the door of the candlelit long room, to stare. The staghound Chasco stood as astonished as we for a moment, unable to decide what reality or what phantasm the gray rain brought.

"*Hola?*" Don Vito challenged. He held the dog by the collar.

A reedy sound as if it voiced wilderness came calling from atop the lamed blue roan:

"*Speaks the Ensign!* Carrier of the Banner! The old Ensign, the old Ibarra man! Teclo Paz-z-z!"

Don Vito stepped forward; I held the dog.

The rider came to earth stiffly, with movement like some greatly grown mantis rousing to bend its twig-thin joints and stir.

Beyond the dog's growling I heard again the reedy voice saying, "Ah-h-h, Vito Cantú-ú-ú-ú!"

They embraced each other in the rain, pounding each other's backs like familiars, without dignity.

"Lieutenant of Horse — "

"Ensign — pass into my house! The mess is serving!"

"Sacred Stomach of Tegucigalpa — "

"And Timbiqui!"

"And Mother of the Remedies! In this beggar's *conducta* of donkeys! The Indian we have yonder, Vito, he will tend it if you show him where, and the pack-loads — or show me, if you please!"

Don Vito commanded El Curaca, who grinned, making a salute bareheaded in show of respect for a familiar who embraced Don Vito Cantú. "Shelter and

Don Teclo Paz

safeguard those packloads, Rivas. Tend and feed the beasts and the Indian. — Do you remember this blue roan?"

"Lightning Forks of Bárbola, we certainly put the Cross-Enflanked I on *this* hip at Guatimape!"

"Exactly."

"My roan is lame," the reedy voice spoke. "My Indian is singular. Very singular. A horse and an Indian from *north of Paquimé!*"

"Help me, God!"

"Rivas! After supper bring the Indian of the Señor Ensign to my kitchen. And give the roan corn!"

We walked into the house, at the heels of Don Vito and this wayfaring Señor Ensign who himself was most singular!

In our candlelight he removed his queer tall hat. It had a sodden great hawk feather stuck erect in its frazzled band. This Carrier of the Banner uncloaked his rain-dark, wilderness-bitten shoulders. We stood in his presence as he came to table.

Wounds of battle healed in times long past had loptopped his left ear, drooped his left eye, broken his nose, put a curve of scar across the freckled flesh of his balding skull. His eyes gazed at us, from their unlike sockets, with attentive and intense steadiness. His nose seemed, below the break, of that notable Spanish length and shape to smell presence of raw silver or gold from great distance.

Don Teclo Paz, whose surname meant Peace, was served supper of much meat and more than one tot of the special Jérez for festival, sitting at his host's right hand and addressing himself to victuals with the appetite of a man who had ridden far.

Finishing our own suppers, we sat bemused not merely by the wayfarer's battered presence but by the vibrancy of the voice emitted from such a lean and scraggly throat pipe. The reedy timbre of its utterance was not unpleasantly tempered by some slight degree of huskiness as if a thousand horseback leagues had raised dusts no brandies might clear.

When we had done with our meal the strange Indian was escorted into the long room. His body had a wiriness like the steel spring in a wheellock; he wore a ragged clout and shirt, hide sandals, and he kept his hat on his head, like a badge, we found, and meaning no discourtesy. His hat was a study. Whereas his master's was immensely tall of crown, the Indian's was squat. His master wore hat brim upturned. The Indian's sagged down all around. His master's hat feather was large. The Indian's was of a nicely calculated smaller size, though similar. He had fastened to it by means of a string threaded from his cactus-fiber hatband a small Cross wrought of copper, an evident talisman and notable possession.

"His hat, you see, makes his mark for him," Don Teclo Paz said. "Whoever of you has seen an Indian under such a Christian hat!"

Don Vito asked the Indian, "You speak Spanish?"

The Indian swallowed and his neck's apple bobbled. "Little," he said, peering straight with his strange black eyes at his questioner.

"I am Don Vito. How are you called?"

"Santelmo."

"How are your people, your tribe, called?"

"Abrach." Then, pointing a finger to his own shirt front, he indicated himself. "*Not* Abrach." He removed his finger, and again indicated himself anew, in the same manner as before. "*Kill* Abrach." Then, using the same indicating finger, he touched Don Vito Cantú's doublet, pointing. "*Kill* Abrach." There was great solemnity in it. With his indicating finger he touched the Cross on his hat. "Christian."

"I gave him this name of Santelmo," Don Teclo Paz said. "I so named him. His eyes. He possesses heathen knowledge. And tongues. Be certain. Do not doubt it, Vito. This Indian has value. Very great value. For your discernment in due course."

[91]

The Indian stood silent.

I thought it might be true that there did dwell in this Indian's midnight eyes a gleam of Saint Elmo's flame. I believed I saw it, a glint of foxfire. It may have been the odd sound of the rain that caused me oddly to believe that I saw it. The raindrops were dripping somewhat through our earthen roof, into the clay pots we had earlier positioned upon the floor. Their patterings tapped small drum taptoos saying Abrach, Abrach, Abrach.

"Nor does he steal," said Don Teclo Paz.

"Good," said Don Vito.

"He will sleep with the packloads." Then Don Teclo Paz directed to Santelmo some Indian words unknown to us, and Santelmo was dismissed from the room. He left us solemnly, without sound, while night rain tapped into clay pots with cadence of tongues not discovered.

Then Don Vito spoke, it seemed for all of us, saying, "I do not doubt this Indian is singular, this Abrach Indian of Saint Elmo who walks with you to our Acuichál, old Carrier of the Banner! Permit me to say something. For harvest of all your carryings now I hope the banner you carry is great and good fortune which is betokened by those many packloads of tightly sewn rawhide buckets! I hope you arrive among us

the
Indian Santelmo

with something for yourself! Though you have not said it. And may not choose to say. Which we would understand, be sure of it!"

"Vito Cantú, I arrive with something, be sure of it! Though I state plainly: it is not in those rawhide buckets. That is something else." He looked around the room, at us. "I feel the inquiries." He looked around again. "Tell me, Vito, this room holds a disciplined company? Do we support here any waggletongues that later we might be compelled to extract by means of a dull dirkblade?"

The spikes of Don Vito's mustachios moved, as they did when he smiled. "The company is disciplined, Ensign."

"I believed it was. Those rawhide buckets carry garbage. King's garbage, as we say, receiving a few *escudos* for it, perhaps with a *castellano* and another *excelente* thrown in, for the buying of a new hat. I bring those buckets along with a personal inquiry. Is Don Cirilo Fraga, of the pleated linen collars, yet treasurer and royal accountant of the works at San Martín?"

The spikes of Don Vito's mustachios moved again. "He is."

"Requiring more than a dull dirkblade to remove him, eh, or to open his mouth, for that matter! This garbage is for Don Cirilo. Who needs it, loves it, and pays for it. Since our Sacred Cesarean Catholic Majesty the good Señor Don Felipe, whom God preserve and greatly prosper, has made it so difficult and so costly, Christ save us, to acquire that garbage! Which, as every Spanish owl now knows, *all* comes only by royal fiat in well-sealed royal parcels from the royal mines at Almadén in Spain; thence across the sea in royal ships, to the hands of those royal treasurers who account the King's Royal Fifth and who slave so pitiably here in these remote Indies to keep enough of necessary garbage on hand to be able to work the patio muds! Eh? So I bring a little. I speak of quicksilver. No man here will speak of it again. The good gray grandsons of Balaam's braying ass, whom Santelmo persuades with a crooked club, will remove the rawhide buckets shortly! For the sake of some poor and profitless treasurer, Sainted Backsides of Badajoz-z, and Bogo! And don't mistake me. Santelmo and I sweated that mercury out of a cinnabar the color of Christ's Blood in a godless cañon on the godless edge of the world!"

There was certain extravagance, which I do not gloze for propriety's sake, in his mode of speech.

"Changing attention to something else, Vito. Of considerably more public news and interest, around

Santa Bárbola. Have you by chance had travelers from there lately?"

"Lately, we have had the curate Gaspar Buendía from San Martín. And we have our Toribio here, this one, who came to us with the Ibarra *conducta* from Mexico, in Lent."

Don Teclo Paz regarded me. "Mm. You are working with the horses?"

"No, sir. With the cows."

"I thought I saw you bearing resemblance in feature, somewhat, to Francisco de Ibarra. When he was your age. As to that, be just half as good a man as he, young one, and people will doff their hats as you pass by!"

He turned his eyes again to Don Vito and said, "You mentioned a curate. So will I. It appears that a Franciscan by the name Agustín Rodríguez there at Santa Bárbola, and aching for martyrdom, intends to lead a party of religious as far north as there are souls to save. They say he has the authentic influence, not only with that new viceroy but with his Holy Office. For a formal *entrada*, I mean with paper of permission and mission signed in the King's name! The entire fandangle. The first since the elegant Paco Vásquez Coronado ruined himself and a quantity of men and horses finding nothing up there.

"Also at Santa Bárbola is a newcomer captain. Sán-chez Chamuscado. Who states absolutely and without doubt he is going as leader of a military unit to protect those clucking friars. They expect the big paper and the funds next year; they say they will start by this time next summer. Fortune to them! And what they would know, if I but told them! That which the Indian Santelmo and I know and have seen with our eyes. Sweet Sainted Carambola! This Chamuscado has not even set foot to either bank of the River of the Flow-ers!"

"And you, Ensign? The River of the Flowers?"

"I found it."

"No! When?"

"Lately. It is there."

"Where? Why did we miss it? How did we miss it? In direction, on a course from Paquimé, where was our error?"

"We were too far west, we had wrong conceptions! We missed it by a full sixty leagues, we were not even close. In those mortal sun-cursed waterless marches too far west. The River of the Flowers has its source hardly ninety leagues from where we sit at this table. The truth is, that source is south and east of what is now Santa Bárbola. Not north and west, as Don Francisco supposed, and we with him. I myself have ridden the

entire course of the River of the Flowers. All of it, following it north.

"And hear now. When I tell you. It meets and joins
a river which is the one we sought and did not find in
'66. It makes the River of the Flowers the trickle of a
dry donkey's voiding! Hear me further! The big one
flows *from* the North. On margins of this grand unknown river's enormity the blue roan horse has carried
me upon deserts of sand, meadows of grass, tree-cov-
ered hills. Passage to the North! Dreamed of, now
found! I have been there. And far beyond the far side
of the unknown river. Where this neck was bending
back more, where these chin whiskers were tilting
higher, to put these eyes on the Mariner's Star. *North!*"

We sat not now bemused but enchanted.

"Vito Cantú? You doubt? Ask Santelmo! No, but
do not ask him. We will take you there. When you
know!"

"When I know what?"

"When you know that which I intend to tell you.
That which I have seen with these eyes staring. There
beyond the unknown river."

"You saw minerals, Teclo Paz. I am sure of it.
You — may have seen what is said to exist. The cities.
With the houses of great height. Did you?"

"I saw them. But that is not why you will go. *For*

I know you well, companion-at-arms. You will go only
when I tell you what else I saw!"

Now the eyes in the unlike sockets were lighted
with a fantast's gleam. I felt sudden odd dread such eyes
might spill heavy shining quicksilver droplets as tears.

"Mysteries do not beckon me, Teclo Paz."

"Not mysteries. I saw with these eyes a horse carrying upon its branded hip the Cross-Enflanked I. I saw
this horse, its shoeless hooves worn to the quick, in the
leaf-bowered manger of an Abrach Indian cacique.
This horse in the hands of savages. This horse fed
from painted bowls of ceremony filled with beans of
mizquitl and fresh grass cut with stone knives. This
dappled dun Ibarra horse receiving homage of drums
and claypipe music like ritual for some golden reliquary
built to house all Satan's power. Listen to me well,
Evaristo Rodrigo Cantú, I saw more. I saw our stolen
remnant of the Guatimape horse herd. Up there! And
I saw the whoreson basilisk turncoat renegade Basilio
Ro trading Ibarra horseflesh for Indian slaveflesh and
barbarous knowledge concerning a great vein of gold
beyond the river! Up there!"

I had never seen the fire of rage in Don Vito's eyes.
We saw it. I had never heard the ice of hatred in his
voice. We heard it.

He said only: "Basilio Ro."

His mouth moved very slightly, saying it. One lock of his gray hair fell very slightly farther over an ear. Nothing else moved.

"Leave me," came the command. "All but the ensign. I will hear him further." His eyes were upon us. "And your own mouths will remain closed. Among yourselves. Among all. Your mouths well closed! Now, good night."

In my room, on my bed of sheepskins and straw, sleep was long in coming. As it came, I heard yet the tap-pattering of the rain of Saint John Baptist's Day. I believed I heard yet the reed-voice, cadenced now to taptoos of quicksilver droplets, falling in foxfire.

I awoke in some faint pause of time between the death of night and birth of day, and heard no rain.

A thin light of morning arrived, but the sun's face was shrouded in cloud when Joaquín Ripalda and I received our work orders from El Curaca and walked to the horse pen for our mounts.

Mud was deep and adhered thickly to our boots. In the damp unwonted chill of such a dark June morning, rawhide *lazos* were stiff, saddle pads and saddle seats were wet with yesterday's soaking, and horses enlivened by the cool were impetuously buoyant.

In the great dampness of the air, Ripalda spoke dryly. "Not exactly the day for wearing leather armor against arrow shots. Or sparking powder in a harquebus pan," he said. Old times of soldiering were at the edge of his mind; I felt it sharply when he added, "God the Lord, this morning it's good to hear the grass in its growing and greening!"

At the saddle shed we saw the *domador* Young Lope, preparing for his own day's work, with *jáquimas* hung over his shoulder.

All three of us were among those who had sat in the candlelight of the long room the night before; all three of us now felt the constraint of Don Vito's command. We greeted each other with certain absurdity, not mentioning, yet also mentioning, what was uppermost in our minds. For in fact the light of this day had not succeeded in making foxfire and quicksilver a fable.

"Still sleepy, Ripalda?"

"Wide awake, man. Like the horses."

"A good horse is an early riser."

"A good horse goes early to bed."

"They say a good horse talks with his ears."

"They say a good rider answers with his hands."

"Eloquent and elegant."

"Sainted Backsides — "

"You mean Blessed Backsides — "

"I mean of Badajoz-z-z. And Bogo!"

"But you don't talk to ponies like that!"

"Who else can I talk to?"

"Thy eloquent self, *domador*."

"It would not be elegant, because I know the replies. Listen, Ripalda, old *vaquero*. When you get out in those mud bogs. This morning with your cows. Talk to them. You will enjoy it. Say nothing to our Toribio. Not he, that eloquent and elegant lad! Just talk to the cows. Ask them. Without any harm. Ask them if they also tasted the Powders of the Mother Celestina last night!"

We were all grinning.

"Powders of the Father Flagbearer," Ripalda said. "You'd better move along to your ponies, Infant Lope!"

Most of the long day was sunless. All of it was muddy. Some of it was strenuous, and a part of it went ill.

In our circuiting of the drenched pasture that morning Ripalda and I found two cows and one calf so bogged in mire we were compelled to employ *lazos* to free them, and we did so without mishap, extricating them from their floundering. Past midafternoon we confronted a different case when we came upon a heavy herd bull trapped in a deep and sticky ooze at the margin of an arroyo's silty backwash. Near to exhaustion with ponderous effort to lunge free, the bull's prolonged thrashing had served only to sink him deeper into the grip of his own miring.

Aid was not easy to devise or render, even with Ripalda's store of skills.

From a clump of poplars growing two hundred *varas* away we broke off rotten limbs and leafy boughs with our *lazos,* and on horseback dragged all we could get to the morass. Then we dismounted and went into the mud, bootless and bare save for shirt and rolled-up smallclothes, for the dirty work of setting the wood in the mud as a makeshift mat to provide footing and aid for starting the bull toward dry ground. The beast resented our proximity and our labors.

For a sturdy and also removable pulling line we at length managed to pass a doubled *lazo* properly under and around both the horns. Ripalda remounted his horse then, arranging and adjusting the doubled rawhide in a snubbing turn around the apple of his saddle, disposed for a hard pull. Ripalda instructed me in my

Young Lope

part of the task: I was to goad the bull from behind, inciting him to move with the pull of the line when Ripalda gave spur to his readied horse. This he did. I saw the line come taut with the whole strength of the horse straining at the pull and I applied the goad, with a herdsman's shout.

The bull came unlodged violently. I saw the motion in a sudden bobble of the bull forward, then in an instant stumbling lunge of strength sideward — but I saw no more of it. A thick splash of mud deluged me, striking my eyes. I blinked them open, seeing very little. But I heard the unreal silence. I wiped my eyes enough then to see Ripalda already at my side, enough to see the bull's curly-haired muddy face and one muddy horn sticking up out of the ooze, unmoving.

"You hurt?" I heard.

"No." I stood there recovering from daze, spitting mud grains.

"Father Christ!" I heard.

Cleaning at my eyes, I asked what happened.

"Broken neck." I heard him snap his wet fingers.

"How?"

"Like lightning."

"Indeed. *How?*"

"When he stumbled! You didn't see? In the smallest of moments the rope went slacked and the rope came jerked! Sideways on that tired neck and he dropped like a stone!"

"The blame, is it upon us, Ripalda?"

"The blame is upon Satan's horns and hear me, son! We were correct in everything but the luck. The luck was foul. And so is this mud. And the bull had luck more foul than we, Father Christ!"

Ripalda reached into the mud, unloosing the turn of the rawhide from around the dead bull's horns. We got ourselves out of the churned muck and found an unroiled puddle in which to wash ourselves somewhat and especially to bathe the grit from my watering eyes. By the time we were clothed again and had mounted to ride, the bull's head and horn were gone, sunk from sight.

"Quicksand?" I asked aloud.

"Maybe a little," said Ripalda. "For certain, call it mud. The mud and the luck. As I shall tell Rivas, who will be asking." Ripalda shook his head. A little drying mud crumbled off a wrinkle of his shirt and we rode away.

The fair breeze came from southwestward, bringing wider rifts of welcome blue above our heads. Then shafts of light, raying like a painted glory, sprang from behind clouds low in the west. The last of the long rain moved in a bank of mist to the north, far beyond Acuichál's home-marked hill. For half a league we rode abreast through sunny grass bright as a field of emeralds.

Several times during the silence of the day I had started to say something and I had not said it. Now I spoke, peering north.

"Ripalda. In this disciplined company, and in none other," I began, feeling awkward, "I could open my mouth for a question."

"What question, son?"

"Who is Basilio Ro?"

He was not so startled as I had expected. He said, "You heard. Didn't you? Last night."

"I make no mention of last night. None whatever. I only ask you. That I may go better armed, with knowing! Ripalda, I understand the closed mouth very well. With or without a dirkblade."

"Such a lad!" he said, looking at me.

I looked at him. "Who is Basilio Ro?"

"Mm. You should ask Gonzalo Duro. If you wish to ask."

"Our sergeant's ears were not amongst those present at table when the name Basilio Ro was mentioned: I would not consider asking Gonzalo Duro anything at all. Perhaps I make a breach of faith asking Joaquín Ripalda. I shut my mouth."

"Keep it shut, son." He paused, relenting. "I will open mine, foolishly, for a moment."

Then he spoke.

"Ro was one of the very young ones in that whore-son crowd of Juan Tolosa and Ginés Mercado.

"Maybe you know Tolosa was with Don Diego in the discovery of the Zacatecas mines. Maybe you know Mercado was the one who believed he had a mountain of solid silver at Guadiana, and found out it was only a mountain of very pure iron.

"When Mercado was ambushed and sent to Hell at Sombrerete, and when the bad blood began between Tolosa and Don Diego, the Lieutenant Basilio Ro cleared out for a while. He went on the unfortunate pearl hunt, in the old faction of Nuño de Guzman, that greatest of whoresons, among the Shark Indians on the Vermilion Sea. Ro got back alive. They say Ro was brave, those days, and this was his virtue. He became an Ibarra man. It was before my time.

"Thus I tell you, Toribio de Ibarra.

"It seems that the Governor and Captain General Don Francisco de Ibarra gave Basilio Ro the power to sound drum and fife and unfurl the banner and do all things which may be done by captains in the army of His Majesty and likewise gave him power to name en-signs and sergeants and other officers of his company.

And likewise, Basilio Ro was named camp master of the force in the field under the command of Don Francisco in his campaign to conquer Tôpia.

"The camp master soon proved to be insubordinate, reckless, brutish and a misfortune to the troops, they say. Deepest trouble developed when Ro was given a picked company and charged with a mission to find passage over rugged and forsaken sierras of terrible darkness and mountainous thickets.

"Ro unjustly accused the twenty Indian guides of treachery in leading him into an impassable gorge, and he then proceeded — in the Captain General's absence and without authority — barbarously to hang all twenty Indians to the same tree! It was an act so gross against justice, against all the Indians of Tôpia, and against nature, that the tree's green wood and fine leaves dried up that very day and died, in visible protest to God Almighty! Gonzalo Duro saw it. He was there.

"When the Captain General came on and learned of Ro's cruelty and other misdeeds, he called a council, and ordering the camp master before it, reprimanded and censured him for his conduct, which had caused an Indian uprising and much spilling of blood.

"Basilio Ro was not chastened by the censure. It made him arrogant and defiant, there on campaign in the wilderness! Then with a few disaffected officers and men he raised mutiny and that was too much. He and his faction were seized by force and hauled in shackles to jail at the *gobernación*.

"It was before my time. I have been told that it was the Lieutenant of Horse Vito Cantú himself who made the capture of Basilio Ro and disarmed him by his own hands and brought him to Don Francisco.

"The criminal charges were made and Ro was tried duly and condemned to death as a traitor to the royal service. But he was not finished. While they were all waiting, lawfully, for the viceroy's approval of the sentence, Ro and four of his scoundrels broke from jail and escaped. How, who knows! God Almighty knows where they went or how they lived, condemned turncoats, renegades. Fornicators of heathen sluts, slave catchers, prospectors. Beyond reach.

"I will add one thing more. In my time.

"I myself was not at Guatimape when Don Francisco de Ibarra died. I was here at the work camp of Acuichál, at Don Vito's orders, tending a beef herd for the San Martín mines. And this I know: when the horses of Guatimape were brought here, not all of them came. The tally at Guatimape showed two- or threescore Ibarra horses missing. Some of them trained by Cantú's own hand. It was supposed that they had been stolen by the poison-arrow Indians of the high sierra, who eat horses as well as people. Among us here the matter of the missing horses was so delicate that it was never mentioned, but once, in the presence of Don Vito Cantú. That once was enough. You saw him when it was mentioned again, last night? Very well! Is your mouth now closed? Mine is."

"My mouth is very well closed," I said.

When we came in with our part of the herd, we noticed the presence of the lamed blue roan in the stable yard, but we did not see Don Vito Cantú or his guest Don Teclo Paz. The Indian Santelmo was not in evidence. There were no donkeys in the side corral where they had been penned that morning. The toolroom door was opened; the patchwork packsaddles, the poor panniers, the sewn rawhide buckets were gone.

El Curaca Rivas greeted us inside our horse pen and stood by as we unsaddled and set our mounts loose through the gate to the fodder field.

"All well and green in your lower end of the pasture?" he asked.

"Plenty wet!" Ripalda said.

"You went in the mud. And brought some home, I see. Any trouble?"

"At one place, yes. The luck went bad, Rivas. We lost a good bull! The big *golondrino* with the dun nose, the one *bizco* of the left horn." Ripalda gave an accurate and detailed report. He ended it saying, "I hate to fail with my rope!"

"So it happens," El Curaca said, mildly enough. "Neither of you is hurt, which is good. And both of you are wiser, which is good. The wisdom being: to cheat wolves is to promise buzzards. Leave it thus, *vaqueros.*"

"We leave it," Ripalda said. "Tell me, Rivas. Don Vito is gone from Acuichál?"

"Likewise, the guests."

"I saw the blue roan, out there."

"The Señor Ensign now rides the good brown horse Clarín."

"He goes well mounted!"

"In what direction was the departure, Rivas?"

"Down the lane. Further than that I did not inquire."

He regarded us, there in the twilight. Then we went to supper.

Our mouths were well closed, for nearly a week.

Late one afternoon we saw Don Vito Cantú come riding over the rise, returning to Acuichál. He was not alone. At his side came Don Teclo Paz newly clad and without a tatter, mounted on the sweet pacer Clarín. Behind them came Santelmo, *riding!* Though he rode

a black hinny instead of a horse, the Indian was not afoot. The moment we saw this, we could not doubt that a matter of consequence was stirring! Moreover, Santelmo now drove no sorrowful string of donkeys. He was in charge of three big strong mules carrying packs in new panniers, rigged under noticeably new covers, with new rope.

I was one of those who helped stow the packloads in a corner room of the main house. Thus, that evening I saw a part of what the mules carried: three used sets of common soldiers' equipage including cuirass, morion, sword and shield; a pair of harquebuses with their straps and swines, some daggers, bullet bags, gloves, leather breeches; two gunpowder casks fitting in a lidded box pannier; camp tools, horseshoes, nails, lead, fire-stones, steels, match cords; together with a bundle of cotton kerchiefs brightly dyed, a bag of glass beads, a sack of old hawk bells and bits of poor mirrors, a box of gauds, odd gaming cards and trinkets of worthless glitter.

Don Vito himself spread the pack covers over all and came out of the room last, closing the door behind him.

When I arose from the breakfast table next morning and started to depart for the usual work of the day, Don Vito Cantú called to me and I came to him with my hat in my hand.

"Tarry a little, Toribio," he said. "I have told Rivas that you will no longer be riding cow pastures. You will attend me here, if you please. Come along!"

Setting my face to avoid outward display of the sudden high spirit such words caused in me, I followed Don Vito to the sun-touched courtyard, then to the blue-shadowed door of the corner room, where he spoke again. "Be seated," he said, pointing to the bench outside the door. He opened it and entered the room. When he came out a moment later he seated himself on the bench beside me and he unfolded a letter he carried in his hand.

"This is Don Diego's," he said. "The same you de-

livered to me from Coyoacán. Did Don Diego show
you or read you any of it, before he sealed it?"

"No, sir. He did not."

"You know nothing contained in it?"

"Nothing, Don Vito."

"Then I wish you to read it." He handed it to me.
"Now. If you will."

I read it with great care and I need not say with
what intense interest, feeling also this signal mark of
Don Vito's confidence.

When I had returned the letter into his hand he
said, "I think it most proper for you to have read it in
my presence at this time. Before I ask a question."

"Yes, sir?"

"Would you ride north with me, Toribio de
Ibarra?"

I did not find it possible to keep emotion from the
answer I made. I believe my words were, "Nothing
could be greater honor, to be asked, and nothing could
be greater obligation, to go."

I remember Don Vito's reply, exactly. "Good," he
said. "You are asked. You will go." The spikes of his
mustachios moved. "Whether you get back is another
matter. Understand that? Whether any of us get back."

"Who will go, Don Vito? That is to say, who
else?"

"Don Teclo Paz and his Indian. Yourself. Myself. And two more, strong, young enough, and faithful. The *domador* Young Lope. Our Vizcayan *vaquero* Joaquín Ripalda. Who incidentally can smell a spring of water farther than the ensign can smell a mine of gold. We will muster a great crowd of six, mounted and armed."

"Six," I said. "Yes, sir."

"Listen, lad. Any horseman knows how a light hand is not a poor hand! We cannot go in force. Very well. We will make our weakness our strength. Our speed will be our hope. Our horses will be our salvation —

"Be advised of something more, Toribio, and thenceforth frame all talk accordingly: we will be no consortium of discoverers displaying paper of permission or banner of authority on this small northern ride. We will be in fact exactly what we are, five Ibarra men guided by an Indian, in civil guise and with civil right to make such circuit of the North as we may find possible or advisable for the sake of hunting minerals. Or livelihood. On Nueva Vizcaya's frontier. You have the name Ibarra and I believe you understand."

"Yes, sir."

"Meanwhile, we all have work, those who go and those who stay! Ten thousand matters to foresee now and not regret later. Arranging with Rivas and the Old Lope the responsibility and the performance of all the necessary husbandry here at Acuichál during our absence. Equipping ourselves. Our horses. Our pack animals. I tell you now, Toribio, the success of our ride may be largely forewrought by our own right preparation here during the coming days!

"I suggest that you begin this morning by assembling every item of your own present equipage, including horse and saddle and bridle and *lazo,* everything ready for my critical inspection before midday. My own next business this morning is a visit to our saddler sergeant, who will be the busiest man at Acuichál for a while now. He is already the angriest one, that he cannot go! I wish he could, I wish old Duro were twenty years younger. He and I both!" I was already on my feet when Don Vito Cantú arose from the bench. "Tomorrow morning," he said, "I will have Ripalda show you and the Young Lope how a soldier handles and fires a harquebus. I hope he remembers!"

Thus six well-equipped and well-prepared mounted men with three mules and three spare saddle horses bearing trim packs set out from Acuichál in the midsummer dawn of Saint James's Day, headed north.

Though we traveled in summer's heat we traveled also in the season of the dog days' great thundershowers when grass was good and waterholes were freshened and held plenty so that the time was to our advantage, carefully calculated by Don Vito Cantú, for maintaining the strength of our horses and for making the routine of our daily marches shorter and easier from water to water.

Each night we picketed our dozen animals close in camp and by water; at first daylight we would allow them to go light-haltered for an hour or so of grazing under watchful guard that they might not wander or come to harm; at vespertime, the same, while we made camp; and sometimes at our nooning if we found some midday shade for our own hour's ease under a likely tree or high rock. In our saddles for eight hours, more or less, we moved a good ten leagues each day without fatigue for any.

As the days passed we grew increasingly proficient in performance of our duties, well and smoothly ordered by Don Vito Cantú.

Young Lope was charged with the care of the eight horses at picket line and at grazing; while the Indian Santelmo was responsible for the care of the hinny, which he valued even more than his hat, and the three mules with whom he seemed to have established some heathenish understanding.

Joaquín Ripalda and I were assigned the evening's making and the morning's breaking of the camp, with its attendant chores.

Don Teclo Paz, such a thin gentleman, demonstrated surprising interest and skill in matters at the cook pot and our victualing. He forthwith became our hunter, as well as our guide, and showed himself to be in fact a redoubtable marksman at deer or hare in distances up to fifty *varas*, using the short Spanish crossbow and the leather bag of honed quarrels he carried handy on his war saddle. Don Teclo was also our overseer, with a muleteer's sharp eye for balance, at the daily packing and lashing of the packloads.

Don Vito Cantú as our commander gave his ready mind and both his ready hands to all matters of our marches.

We made a good company there in wilderness and

I do not hesitate to say that our Ibarra horses — all of them stallions — had no equal in New Spain: Don Vito on the gray-dappled Tordillo, son of the Gran Tordo and the same I had seen reined by the one hair plucked from the mane; Don Teclo on the brown pacer, the splendid Clarín; Young Lope on a seven-year-old bright bay named Alacrán, a horse rein-trained by the Old Lope, and a marvelous quick turner in a gallop; Ripalda on a very stout dun he of course called Vaquero, black-maned, linebacked, with handsome zebra stripes on the legs, and it may be the best *lazo* horse at Acuichál; myself on my faithful Caobo from Toluca. The three spare horses carrying packloads were all strong saddle mounts well gentled to any work required.

During the first days of our steady northing it seemed much to me as if we might yet be riding familiar pastures, traversing lonely but not unknown lands, the same as Acuichál.

We saw no Indians either of the tamed or of the wild kind. We met no person whatsoever, though the region through which we passed had been trodden by Christians. Indeed, hooves and cartwheels had marked the ground with a hint of road, which we encountered in a valley upon the third day, the dim trace of passage leading from Guadiana, seat of the *gobernación*, to

Santa Bárbola's mines, the minuscule cluster of settle-
ments farthest north in all New Spain.

We crossed the roadway's valley, bearing eastward
from it and from proximity to the Santa Bárbola district
of habitancy, at the guidance of Don Teclo Paz and his
Indian, and moving at a good pace.

On the eighth day past noon we came down through
foothills under the eastern face of a wild *serranía* and
onto the opening out of a ravine where some pools of
recent freshet water stood like the beads of a necklace
along the windings of a gray gravel stream bed. We
halted by one of the pools where there was a little shade
and Don Teclo told us with much satisfaction that our
animals were watering now at the River of the Flowers!

I confess it was not as I had imagined it.

That evening we made our camp by a thin trickle
of water flowing north upon a broadening plain, and
we stood our guard watches for the first time through
all the night.

Among the personal belongings I had brought with me from Coyoacán was a small but valued copy book given me by my old preceptor the grammarian Father Jerónimo Cienfuegos, who taught me all I know of letters and gave me all I have of learning, which clearly is little enough. Upon the eve of departure from Acuichál I had pulled two folds of blank leaves from the back of my book in order to have them, with a little wrapped slug of sharpened shot lead, among the small needments I had packed in my saddlebags. Thus at each camp we made I was able to keep count of the days of our journey, entering sometimes additionally a few words or numbers, largely undecipherable to other eyes, as a private aid to recollection if and when my destiny and my horse might return me from the North.

It seemed to me that when our horses' hooves made their printings in the sandy shallows of the flowerless river named for flowers, finally we passed from that which was familiar, crossed some impalpable boundary either of earth itself or of thought itself, and entered into that which was unknown. We arrived North.

The revealed and visible enormity of earth's space and sky's space dwarfed and shrank us, a horseback company, to pinpoint size.

There was less grass along the way. Our pace was slower.

In the sunstruck glitter of the long-lasting days we sat our saddles as if riding adrift, cast from the reasonable confines of countable time and calculable space.

Evening with its reaching shadow came to us as a benison. Morning returned like the swinging open of a hot-fired furnace door.

The frail river's course directed us and its water was our sustainment. On the third day we found it making confluence with two streams from the west and the flow was increased.

That day we saw Indians; we came upon them at their fishing in the river and they fled to hide from us, timid and wild and nearly as fleet as deer.

These people, we learned from Don Teclo Paz, call themselves Pataros. Their flight was caused by their fear of mounted Spaniards: this tribe was hunted by slave catchers who found a good price for those they caught, carrying them to Christian baptism and bondage in the new mines of Santa Bárbola. The Pataros are a poor people who go naked, though the women cover their privities with a small kirtle of rabbitskin or deerskin. They are not fierce. They prefer living in peace with their own crude idolatry, supporting themselves on fish, beans of the *mizquitl*, roasted stalks of the *sotol* palm, and a little hunting which they practice with bow and arrow.

Through this region we saw some nearly every day, regarding our passage warily from a distance. We were wary also. We knew not how many times unseen but seeing eyes gazed upon us, far or near.

On the sixth day we saw no Pataros whatsoever: it was the day we passed a weathered stockade strongly

built of willow trunks cut from the riverbank. Don Teclo called it El Xacál and showed us how it was an enclosure used for the holding and taming and guard- ing of the slave catchers' captives brought in from the wilderness, on their way to the forced labor of the mines.

"It goes unused. The stench has left it," Don Teclo said, and spit upon the ground. "This pretty jail is the handiwork of an expert in jails. Basilio Ro, to name him. And to say no more."

The Pataros avoided the entire vicinity. I was glad when we rode on.

The next day, in order to pass around an impassable gap where the river made its way down a defile be- tween steep slopes, we departed from the water's course for a distance of almost five leagues over rough hills. Traversing the sharp flinty ridges, three of our animals threw shoes, my horse among them. We abandoned nothing so valuable as an iron shoe, even though worn, and I put Caobo's in my saddlebag; later we back- trailed a thousand *varas* to find one of the muleshoes, for Santelmo did not see or hear it come off.

While we were halted, Don Teclo pointed to a ledge colored with evidence of mineral out upon our left. "Cinnabar over there," he grinned. "Eh, San- telmo?"

[135]

Santelmo paid attention only to tying the found muleshoe very securely to his saddle, saying nothing.

"Mercury. And other white metal, nearby," Don Teclo said. "Silver without doubt. And not worth the misery. Until a few more Christians are living a few leagues closer!"

The next day, which was the fifteenth from Acuichál, we did not ride but lay over encamped near the river's water and a pocket of good bunch grass, to shoe and rest our horses, rearrange kits and furbish weapons.

Don Teclo chose to saddle his Clarín, take up a light-shafted lance, and use part of the day on a solitary ride "to hunt nearby," he said. He returned with one rabbit and one of his saddlebags filled with ore samples from the mineral ledge. "I have been thinking about that silver," he said. He put some of the ore in the fire under our stew pot, "to cook a little." With a grimace he added, "It shows poor value."

That night, without the fatigue of a dozen leagues under a blazing sun, we sat talking after supper.

Twenty *varas* away our dozen animals dozed quiet and contented at the picket line, with Santelmo standing the first watch of the night. Closer by, our packs and panniers were neatly ranged, our weapons ready and in reach. A nearly full moon came climbing from the sharp black line of the sierra far to the east, and we allowed the light of our cookfire to shrink to the glow of a few red coals. In the still air the lacy leaves of the *mizquitl* were motionless. Night sounds of insects, and of a frog by the river's life-giving moisture, pulsed the silence.

"They call it the Valley of Goodness," said Don Teclo. "The Indians in their own tongue named it thus: Valley of Goodness. North of the Great North River. Our eyes shall see it.

"I myself have been to its threshold, and looked upon it, but I have not yet entered into the Valley of Goodness. Santelmo has.

"It is a valley of his people, Otmaco Indians. As to these, these are kinsmen and congeners of the Abrach, they are a branch of the Abrach. In fact, the only difference may be that the Otmacos live near the great river and plant maize, having houses by their fields; while the Abrach live north on the grass plains, hunting midst the great herds of the wild shaggy cows, living in tents of the cowhide, wandering like gypsies, with dogs trained to drag the burdens.

"Some Otmacos and some Abrach live both ways, farming south, hunting north. I do not fully understand their arrangements. Perhaps none do, for they have quarrels among themselves, even some wars among their caciques, whom they call *sibiyes*. Santelmo was in fact a young *sibiye*. It was one of these war-ax and stone-knife family feuds which caused his exile, and gave him his feelings of rancor and vengeance, before I very fortunately saved him from his own kinsmen there beyond the river and brought him southward and had him sprinkled all proper by the missionary at Rayos and gave him his present Christian position.

"I am grateful, in my turn, to Santelmo. And I say it. He brought a gift to my hand and provided me with the great hope of my life. From the Valley of Goodness. I have shown what it is to Don Vito. He has seen it, and knows. The rest of you, Lope, Ripalda, Toribio, have not seen it and do not know. But. Now you shall. Why not?"

We saw him unfold his leanness, arising from the ground, and watched him walk with spurs clinking to his saddlebag. "In this light of the moon, Vito! A time to see it!"

It was wrapped in a much wrinkled kerchief of silk.

[138]

When he had seated himself among us again, he un-swathed it with a ceremonial carefulness, then displayed it uncovered in his open hand. "You see?"

It was a lump almost as big as the apple on my sad-dlebow.

Don Teclo put it into my palm. By the weight I knew the richness: I hefted the massy pull of gold. Lifting and tilting it close to my eyes, I peered at the rough matrix of the mother ore embedded and em-bossed with mellow gleam, veined and flecked heavy with luster in the brightness of the moon.

"It was larger," Don Teclo said. "When I with sorrow found it necessary to chip off a chunk — in or-der to pay for those miserable donkeys, at Rayos — the separated piece hung connected with the rest by a soft and bending little tangle of pure golden wires! As if it did not wish to leave us!"

Lope held the great heaviness upon his palm. "Fa-ther of Fatties," he called it! His white teeth in the moonlight showed a gleam bright as the very gold in his hand.

Joaquín Ripalda examined it gravely. "The true mine of the true Quivira," he said. "Like the dream old Duro used to talk about. Maybe."

"Mark me, Ripalda," Don Teclo said, "a captain of grand category, Vásquez de Coronado, with three hun-

[139]

dred durable Spaniards in a thousand long leagues of looking never found a faintest proof of a thing like this which you have held in your hand!"

"There in that valley, Señor Ensign, how much of the rock could there be like this piece? This great one! Much?"

"I will tell you, Lope. You ask. It is a ledge. With the lode exposed! So that in the afternoon, when there has been a rain shower, and the western sun touches the washed ledge, it glistens from afar. Santelmo says. I have not seen it yet. Sweet Carambola! But how it beckons and lures. How it enchants. A greedy fellow like that Cirilo Fraga at San Martín would wet himself, both legs, at mere sight of mother mineral so rich!"

"The Indians mine it, Señor Ensign?"

"No."

In the stillness of the moonlight a coyote, a small and furtive kind of wolf very common to the region, cried far away, as if lamenting. The horses at the picket were vaguely restive, uneasy for a moment, then quiet with Santelmo standing by.

"Why do the Indians not mine it?"

"They condemn it, as being accursed. Santelmo says. In their heathenism. In their ignorance."

Don Teclo offered the gold to the hand of Don Vito, who had spoken no word; he did not take the lump. "Thank you," he said. "I have examined it. By day."

Don Teclo rewrapped it in silk, replaced it in the saddlebag, and buckled it in. A coyote wolf cried again farther away, and was answered.

"Valley of Goodness," Don Teclo said then, gazing at the moon. "I do not vaunt it. But I ask, who gains greatly without risking greatly? And I say, companions, I would find it good to live content. Searching no longer. At ease for a little time, before I die."

There was a long silence. Finally Don Vito spoke, with the commander's reserve and the commander's propriety which he unfailingly showed to each of us in camp.

"I go north to claim horses bearing the Ibarra brand," he said. "In a few days we will see the North River, and the first Otmacos, Santelmo's people. To-morrow it might be well for us to begin the wearing of war harness, helmet and breastplate, on the alert. I should like to convey to these Indians our own recti-tude at first sight and first meeting. We will use kind-ness if we can, our weapons only if we must, and in all circumstances we will use our horses. We are horse-men. *Jinetes!* I should like to open these Indians' eyes and ears to a power of the Spanish crown and to a character of the Spanish subject antipodal and implacable to the viciousness of a Basilio Ro! We shall meet him, I believe. At the so-named Valley of Goodness, or thereabouts. I assure you that goodness and Ro are not bedfellows!"

I had the second watch of the night, on duty until the moon was halfway westered. I felt no drowsiness, thinking.

We rode north now through a greatest desolation of rainless terrain, enclosed on every side by the unknown.

All around us range beyond range of barren *serranía* stood hazy with heat and silence, iron-blue ghosts of mountains against blue iron sky. The iron shoes of our horses engraved harder ground. The iron shine of our morions and cuirass plates caught the iron glare of the sun; the metal we wore flashed out signal glints of our advent upon awesome reaches of dry space — and the river led us. It was a thin thread of life sewn by the iron of some transcendent needle across the dust-crusted iron of a sun-smitten world.

Then one afternoon with the iron glare angled sharp upon our left shoulders and upon our rein hands we came up under the foothills of the Sierra of the Big Crest, as we named it, and we saw the first Otmacos. Santelmo pointed to them not three hundred *varas* ahead of us. They were standing in the rocks atop the hump of a bare hillock, a score of archers afoot, armed ready and watching us. They had been reading for a long while the signals of the sun flashing on the iron we wore.

Don Vito commanded us. "Halt in full view. Lope, Ripalda, Toribio, remain halted with the pack animals in hand. Our ensign and Santelmo will come forward with me, to show and to tell these first ones that we come in peace and as friends."

Riding with them for a short way, Don Vito spoke instructions to Don Teclo and the Indian. Then he left them stationed at his back. He moved out well ahead and advanced toward the Indians alone.

We watched him riding forward upon that bare ground at this savage farthest rim of our known earth — and we saw suddenly Don Vito Cantú in display of horsemanship which was godlike beyond power to describe.

[143]

The dappled gray Tordillo at no visible or audible command entered into the airy step, the flowing turn, the sideward glide and turn again of a strangely wonderful dance cadenced to a music its own tempo magically summoned. In it Don Vito Cantú with armor gleaming doffed his helmet as if saluting a king.

We watched the dance move forward across wilderness ground, through flowery corridors, through convolving figurations long and sweetly paced to issue at last from the windings of a wizard's maze.

By the foot of the hillock where the savages stood unmoving, with their bows and arrows in their spellbound hands, the final *passage* of the dance came to a close. In a weightless *levade* of greatest grace Tordillo rocked back and rose high on hindquarters. Staying up incredibly, neck arched, forequarters to the sky in salute, the noble Tordillo made the complete turn of an airy and perfect pirouette, then came down to earth with infinite slow ease, to stand as still as the Indians, facing them. Don Vito Cantú, equestrian enchantment created, with decorous sweep of right arm replaced helmet to head, and sat silent, motionless on motionless horse. Then Don Teclo and Santelmo rode forward to the foot of the hillock.

The Otmacos, affected already, were startled to have a mounted man dressed in a weathered Spanish brig-

andine, a cotton clout, hide sandals, a frazzled hat with
a feather — riding a strangely long-eared horse with
a strangely short-haired tail — call out to them in their
own tongue! They came in peace from their hillock.
Don Vito signaled us to advance with the pack animals and join with the meeting.

The Indians were squatted in a semicircle facing
Santelmo, who squatted like them. They heard him
and answered him gravely in the words of their own
tongue, glancing often at the silent Don Vito Cantú
standing by the gray horse. Santelmo spoke and made
signs with our ensign, interpreting; Don Teclo in turn
relayed to us the gist of the information the Indians
gave.

To the Great North River's confluence with the
River of the Flowers it was a long day's march for a
man afoot, not so long for a man on a horse.

The fording of the river near the junction was now
dangerous. The water was high in the big river, it being the season of rains in the North.

There was a crossing four leagues north of the junction which was passable now. It was the crossing called
The Stones.

No, there were no other horses or horsemen in the
vicinity now, none. They were at the Valley of Goodness, perhaps.

That valley was ten days away, for a man on foot. With horses, less.

No, they knew nothing of the valley, they had not been there. Never. They did not wish to go there. It was not their district. Their own houses and fields were up the big river, on this side of the big water. Not far from The Stones.

Yes, they had been watching us arrive since the sun stood highest, since midday. Two suns ago a Pataro had come to the river *ranchería* to warn them that slave catchers were coming again, and they had come out to see if this was true, and now they had already sent a runner back to the river to spread the alarm. They had sent the runner when we were far, far in distance. Before they were able to give measure to our numbers or our conduct.

They wished to say that if we came to enslave Otmacos, they would find means to destroy us.

But now they wished to say that they did not believe that the cacique with the gray mustachios and the gray horse displayed the countenance of the evil they had expected. He appeared to be a very great lord of the South, greater beyond any that they had ever imagined. They had felt the spell he cast upon them, they still felt it, how he came riding with powers of magic upon a dancing horse. They sought peace with the evident power of the gray cacique and the gray horse.

Don Vito stepped forward with the music of his spurs at his heels. He solemnly presented this *sibiye* and chief spokesman with a scarlet kerchief, a playing card, and three good bright brass hawk bells, telling him through Santelmo that he must let all Otmacos know that we came in peace toward them and at war with any who would enslave them. Their cacique, greatly pleased, dispatched three runners now, each carrying one of the hawk bells, to countermand the previous alarm and tell the river people we came as friends. The remaining Otmacos made a little camp not far from ours, watching all we did. At our evening meal we gave them meat from our stew pot and a few corn cakes.

These savages had well-made bodies and covered their nakedness, wearing clouts of tanned hide. Their bows were somewhat Turkish in shape, all reinforced and very strong, strung with good cord of sinew which Santelmo said came from the wooly cows of the North. The arrows were pointed with white flint and nicely fletched. The aspect of the Otmacos was warlike. They cut the hair above their foreheads very short; on top they let it grow two fingers long and dressed it with a bright red greasy clay so that it made a topknot, to which they fastened a few feathers of white and black birds.

That night we stood our watches in pairs, doubling vigilance for our horses and every item of our gear.

The next day, with Otmacos trotting afoot as we rode, we came around the shoulder of the Sierra of the Great Crest and from its slope we looked down upon the valley of the North's great river.

It was as I had imagined it.

My horse Caobo and I paused for a little while there on a stone height all alone; with my gaze turned north into the hugeness of the land whence the river flowed, I saw and I knew the majesty of its passage from realm beyond realm unknown.

We forded the river that afternoon without incident, wading waist deep, leading our horses, then the pack train. The water was exceedingly brown with muddiness. It flowed with a strange silence. We made our camp on the north bank in ample shade of poplars called *alamos;* their large heart-shaped leaves rustled sweetly in a faintest breeze. There was strong grass for the horses.

Many Otmacos and none unfriendly came in from their *ranchería* of fields and wattled huts to our camp, it seemed mainly for the purpose of rendering the homage of gazing at Don Vito and the gray Tordillo.

Clearly, Otmaco tongues had not been idle concerning our commander and his horse.

We saw the first Otmaco women. They wore tanned deerskin bodices fashioned like scapulars, with another deerskin as a skirt, and their hair was long. They came bringing calabashes and baskets of *mizquitl* beans to Don Vito. He gave their men as gifts from his saddle-bag a few iron trifles and a green kerchief. None of these Indians appeared to recognize either Don Teclo Paz or Santelmo in any reference to their previous sally in the region. None provided news of the Valley of Goodness. Don Teclo told us he believed that this was from their reluctance to speak of ill matters, not from their lack of information.

In the Great North River there is a very large and fine-flavored type of fish called *bagre*, with long barbels and no scales. The Indian who received the green kerchief brought Don Vito a *bagre* just caught. It weighed at least a full *arroba*; we baked it in a fire pit dug in the ground and enjoyed it for supper.

Next morning Don Teclo Paz in counseling with Don Vito told us the Valley of Goodness was at least fifty leagues downriver — not up, as I had supposed — from this camp we made near The Stones. Between us and the Valley of Goodness the river's course bent eastward and flowed for many leagues through a very deep, terrible and impassable chasm; our only feasible approach to the Valley of Goodness would be to enter it through its upland portal, he said. Accordingly, it was necessary for us to make our way now in an eastward direction, riding for several days generally parallel to the river's eastward course but at considerable distance north of where it flowed.

We left the grand river and rode with our faces toward the morning sun. Santelmo chose our way, showing evident and confident familiarity with the pathless terrain of our easting, bringing us invariably to rocky waterholes, seep springs and good grass for our camps.

For the first few days, small bands of Otmaco warriors came trotting out to meet and observe us, informed of our passage in the district by messengers from their nearest neighboring *rancherías*. They greeted the armored "gray cacique" on the magic horse with a ceremonious respect, albeit revealing also their curiosity to observe him, and all of us with him. They displayed no outward sign of hostility — and no disposition whatsoever to accompany us even for a short distance eastward. For this reluctance they spoke no reasons to their strange kinsman Santelmo, at least none that he conveyed to us; yet we saw that every Indian we met intended to avoid the region toward which we rode.

There was an uneasiness about it.

We came into uplands of increasing elevation and better air. The foothills of the surrounding sierras were dotted not only by wide stands of *sotol* palms and thickets of prickly *tuna* but by dwarf oaks and cedars on the heights. One afternoon a rainstorm, with some hail, violent lightning and crashing thunder, soaked us and brought refreshing cool. The fragrance of moisture on the cedars was like elixir.

We found much game in these green-leafed highlands: rabbits so foolish they were easily killed by a man with a lance on horseback, though they flew from a man on foot; a kind of bluish-gray small partridge, it seemed by the thousand, and excellent roasted; many deer, including the swift deer-like *antílope* antlered with small upright shafts of black horn. We saw a black bear gaze at us, then shamble away over a rocky hilltop; two nights, during the *modorra* watch when sentinels are drowsiest, our horses and especially the mules were alarmed by a panther lion's scream.

After the cruel sun and desolate solitude of the wastelands south of the great river, this more moderate and somehow less infinite wilderness should have offered us a pleasant relief. This was not the case. We felt a vague but constant menace roundabout us. It was doubtless caused by the uncertainty in our minds as to what might be before us if and when we found horse tracks. On the fourth day of our eastward heading I confess that my own unspoken uneasiness changed to a kind of foreboding, not a cowardice but a feeling of dread; I believe that Lope and Ripalda felt it also, though we said nothing to each other about it.

Two days later, in the glare of noon and with our weapons ready in our hands, we came to the "leaf-bowered manger" of the Ibarra horse Don Teclo had described so vividly the rainy night he came to us. We

saw the manger now, it was there: ruined, leafless, deserted, trackless, blasted with solitude. Weather-whit-
ened horse bones, a ragged piece of stiff horsehide
clearly showing a patch of dun-colored horsehair, lay
strewn over the forlorn ground. Our horses showed
their distaste, snorting. We dismounted, as if we had
come to a monument.

"Where there were drums and claypipe music." The
reedy voice of our ensign cut the silence.

"Nothing since. It seems," Don Vito said, dry.
"Not since wolves had their feasting."

"A dun horse in the hands of Death. Not in the
hands of Indians — " said Lope.

"Maybe the same," said Ripalda.

"Not the same," said Don Vito. "Every horse we
find dead and unable to beget more horses in this savage North gives me cause for thanksgiving!"

The Indian Santelmo raised his arm, pointing it
north, and aimed an eye along his outstretched arm. Using Spanish, he said, "The Abrach and the horses,
north, all north." Then, with the same arm outstretched, he swept it southeast and pointed to a steep
gap between two hills. Speaking in his own tongue, he
shook his head.

Don Teclo said, "He thinks the people are not in
their valley, they are gone with the horses. To kins-

men who hunt the cows and have the great meat to carry on the plains. North."

We stood in the sunlit silence by our horses.

"Basilio Ro," Don Vito said, as if speaking the name to the silence and not to us.

"We shall see," said Don Teclo.

"We shall." Don Vito spit upon the ground.

"Yonder is the threshold to the Valley of Goodness," Don Teclo said. "We have come to it. Santelmo will spy it out for us tonight in the dark."

We made camp behind a hill, with our weapons by our hands, grazing and watering our horses well and supping early.

At nightfall Santelmo prepared for his scout into the valley. He removed his hat and placed it on the fore-bow of his saddle. He divested himself of the weighty brigandine, then his shirt. Stripped to clout and sandals, he buckled on a belt by which he carried a leather-sheathed knife, iron-handled and wickedly sharp. Thus readied he gazed around at each of us; in this twilight his strange eyes were indeed touched with a foxfire, a fathomless savagery. He spoke to his master Don Teclo.

"And when he returns," Don Teclo said in Spanish, "he will need a password. That we may know it is he, here in darkness."

"Let him call out his own name," Don Vito commanded. "Our password is Santelmo."

His sandals treading the ground made no slightest sound. He melted into gloaming without his Christian hat. Night came moonless, black, uneasy.

We kept no campfire alight. Clouds moved and spread in the sky, hiding more and more stars. A wind from the north stirred in sighs across the empty spaces, over the rocky hills, through the dim gap to the valley, down the obscure ravines toward the great river. We waited, all five of us on watch and alert, by our arms and the closed packs and picketed horses.

Cloud swallowed all the stars and hid the clock of the sky. We only guessed at the unwinding of time. It was slow. Winds died, and in the quiet our horses sensing our own feelings shared our restlessness, our unformed expectations. I found myself peering often at Caobo's ears, and at Santelmo's hinny's long ones, to read what news they might be finding in the night around us. The news remained illegible.

"Sons," Don Vito spoke quietly. "Why is it that we all sit here like owls? I assigned myself this watch! The rest of you — take some ease while you can. I will call you, each to stand your guard. Meanwhile, sleep a little."

A few fine drops of rain touched cold on my face

and hands, then none, and the wind stirred again in long night sighings. I would have taken oath that there was no drowsiness in me, waiting for Santelmo's return. Somehow, the enveloping dark closed in upon a nearer dark behind the closed lids of my eyes. I dozed, eased of my peering and listening.

The sky was hazed blue. The sun lacked warmth. I wandered in unnamed trouble and I came walking into a street, it seemed the raw lane between the gaunt buildings at the mines of San Martín. A long file of poor Indians came passing me. They were naked save for dirty rags girthed around their middles. Their bodies were caked with dust from down the stone throat of a mine of gold. I saw the mine, it was a shining ledge under the face of a cliff at the head of the lane. The gold showed. It was not San Martín. The Indians in their rags were weeping. A foreman with a whip in his hand walked at the Indians' backs. He said to me as he passed, "From daily labor to daily bread, these Christians." Then I saw coming from the mouth of the terrible mine a lamed and famished file — not mules, not donkeys — oh, of horses. Each one was burdened with a monster pair of grievous rawhide buckets. As the horses came to me I saw that they wept like the Indians. The horses bore upon their wasted hips a Cross-Enflanked I not burned but slashed with a knife and bleeding like a wound of Jesus on the Cross. I was afraid and I cried out: wakened by a hand of Don Vito Cantú shaking my right arm! With my eyes opened astart — I knew not whether I dreamed yet — or wakened to worse than dream.

A vast light and shuddering rumble filled all heaven and earth. It was not dream: I staggered to my feet, seeing Don Vito, Ripalda, our ensign, Lope, our horses, our camp, the earth and the vault of the sky lit with an uncanny sunless refulgence bright as noon. And the rumbling roar — I heard Santelmo's hinny scream in dread. We stood frozen with our own terror, as did our wild-eyed horses, helpless, quaking in the glare of the heaven-filling light and the doom of the deep-throated sound. Sense beyond thought pierced into me: now had come the Last Day, and Judgment: I knew it! There came quick an instant's growth of shattering roar, a greatest flare of brilliant flash somewhere north — then total dark. The earth trembled beneath our trembling feet. The sound died in echoed lunges of rumble, fading at last to a silence as profound as the dark. Bereft of speech we fell to our knees, crossed ourselves and prayed in our awe as we were able.

Nothing happened.

We rose to our feet.

[163]

Soothing the horses and quieting the mules, we somewhat returned to our wits. And Don Vito busied us. "Build us a fire, Ripalda. Fix that mule's twisted halter, Lope. Fetch us the gourd bottle, Toribio, my throat is dry!"

Never have I found firelight more sweetly welcome. Standing in it, Don Vito said, "Build a good fire, sons. I think the world is so shaken it will take small note of this blaze from a few twigs. And tell me, Ensign, are these heavens in the North commonly so appalling?"

"Holy Mother! I hope not commonly!"

We began to find our voices again.

"It lacks reality." Lope's throat was husky. "In this quiet. This dark."

"It happened," I told myself aloud.

"But what?"

"The most fright possible, speaking for myself."

"We could boast, whose blood ran coldest."

"Don Vito," Ripalda spoke up. "At the time, I believed the Last Hour of the World had arrived. Tell me, did it? Do you suppose? Do you suppose we may be so poorly placed here, so remote, that we did not see the Judgment as it proceeded? Do you suppose we are dead now and already gone to Hell and so far from anything we don't know it yet?"

I saw the spikes of the gray mustachios bobble. "A very interesting question, Ripalda. However. It seems to me we remain on earth. Most authorities state that Hell is instantly recognized by all who arrive there. I believe we are somewhat north of Nueva Vizcaya and alive yet, thanks to God. Let me tell you what I think we have just witnessed. My father must have seen something very like it. He spoke of it more than once, when I was young at Dehesa de Oro. It happened when he was young. On campaign with Hospitalers at Rhodes. He was aboard a vessel coasting Africa on a starry night. And one of the stars came roaring down and fell. He saw it. It struck Africa with a terrible sound and a light bright as the sun. Tonight a star fell. Eh? We could not see it falling because of the clouded sky. But it seems reasonable to me, and the best explanation. A star fell and shook the earth."

"In my opinion, it nearly hit us!"

"I share your opinion."

"Imagine it coming loose, up there. It almost smashed this Valley of Whatever It Is, and us too! A star!"

"Well, if it was a star," Don Teclo Paz said, "it was an important one. And enormous. Listen, Vito, hear me. It may have portentous meaning. Consider it, in

[165]

the minds of heathen savages! The cacique of the dancing horse. Calling down a star from the sky — to give
sign of his power among these people!"

Don Vito answered, "Señor Ensign, you might have
been an Indian wizard if you had not been a Christian
soldier. We shall see how our own Christian Indian is
affected by fearful signs in the heavens. If Santelmo
does return to us now."

"Do not doubt it, Vito. He was, before baptism, an
Indian wizard himself."

We waited for him.

He arrived in the first gray of morning. Ripalda's
vaquero eyes found him first, a vague glide of shadowy
shape in dawnlight stillness, before we heard the password called. He came up to our cookfire and walked
past us in silence, to his hat with the Cross. He put it
on his head, as if in haste, and walked over to his hinny
and patted its nose. Then he turned to us by the fire,
pointing to the sky, and made a grimace pantomiming
fear.

Don Teclo addressed him, pointing also to the sky,
solemnly. "A very great Power," he said. Santelmo answered in words of his own tongue and by the signs he
made with his hands.

"He was stricken with fright of the strangeness,"
came the ensign's reedy voice. "He says he greatly

[166]

wished for this hat of his. In that noonday of the night! He says that he saw again the ledge where the gold is; he saw it shining. In the glow of the light with the world roaring."

"Very well," Don Vito said quietly. "Basilio Ro? Horses? People?"

As to Basilio Ro, he was there. He was in the sickness of gold, his mind gone rabid. All Otmacos knew it. All Abrach knew it.

How did Santelmo know it?

He saw Basilio Ro.

Where? Exactly where?

In front of the bower the Abrach built for him by the great river. It was like the bower of the dun horse, but better. It was more ceremonial. It was built so that from its entrance the ledge with the gold was very plainly in sight.

Enough of the ledge with the gold. It was more important to know how Santelmo found the dwelling of Basilio Ro.

Santelmo knew where the bower would be. He knew and he went.

And by what strange manner of means was it possible for his eyes to see a sick and a mad Basilio Ro?

By the evident strange power of Don Vito Cantú, whose magic could bring moments of noonday into the night! It was by this magic easy to see Basilio Ro, though fearful. He with three slave wives came cringing out from the bower when the great light and the great roar came, and Santelmo was there! He saw them fall upon the ground in their terror, he was very near them. He was near enough to step over and knife Basilio Ro. But fright robbed Santelmo also of strength. He was not able to grasp his knife for the deed, he says.

When darkness and silence returned, his strength returned with it. Enough for Santelmo to call out. The concubines were mad with fear when the unknown voice called out. They groveled. Basilio Ro sat queerly bolt upright on the ground, unmoving, as if stunned rigid in fright or madness or sickness. And Santelmo found growing strength to unsheathe his knife and to hold it in his hand and speak.

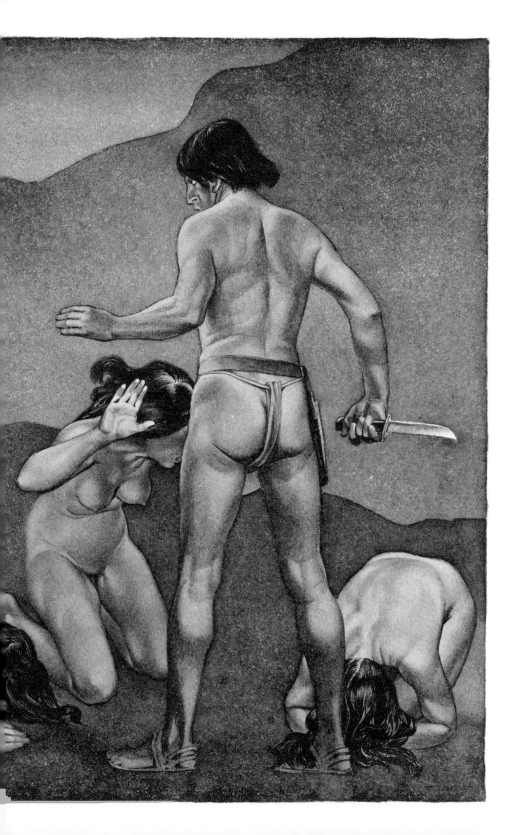

The concubines believed he was some spirit returned from death.

He told them he was.

They groveled, naked, wildly praying him to go away.

He stood there.

He told them he would go away when they had listened to him and spoken answer to all he would ask them. If they lied they would die, he told them; he would take them back with him to the world under the ground, whence he had come, with the great light and the great sound.

They would not lie, they told him, crying.

He would test them, he said. Where were the people of the valley, he asked.

They were all with the Cow Nation, north, by the water of the River of the Cows.

All the people?

All. Save for the three of them. And their master of the bower here, the dark-bearded lord.

And his horses?

Gone out. With the Cow Nation, to the north, like the people.

All the horses?

All.

How many horses gone out? Counting with care on the fingers! How many horses?

Some horses were dead. They had died in the valley, before going out.

I know the dead ones, Santelmo said to the women. I have seen the dead ones in the world below. But those alive yet, how many with the Cow Nation now?

We do not know, we do not lie! Perhaps horses alive to the number of the fingers of four hands. No more, when they left the valley. The others were dead.

Very well, he told them. Why are you here alone in this valley with only your master, the dark-bearded lord?

We were chosen by him to serve him, and given to him by the *sibiyes* of our people, in return for his gift of the great horses to the Abrach. We would be punished by dark powers, we would die, if we forsook him!

Are there others with him here? Are there other lords with beards, other masters from the South carrying the iron tubes that thunder?

There were two. He killed them.

I have seen them both under the ground, Santelmo replied. Then he asked, Why does your lord remain here solitary in the Valley of Goodness, when all others have left it? Why does he do this, why?

They pointed to the ledge where the gold stood in the dark. They said, he guards it. It was given to him by the *sibiyes,* it was what he desired, also in return for the horses. He has the morbid malady of gold. The lords from the South all have it, this sickness.

He will die of it soon, Santelmo told them.

We know this, the concubines said. All Oumacos, all Abrach know this.

All those in the world under the ground know it, Santelmo said. When your lord here is dead from the gold, the people will return and good corn will grow again in this valley. He will die soon.

You lie, came the first words from where Basilio Ro sat immobile in darkness. Whatever you are, you lie, and I say it! I will guard this grandeur of the gold I myself have found, and I myself possess, and Death will not find me! I curse Death, I defy Death, Basilio Ro said. If you are Death — go back with your excrement in your mouth to your poor world under the ground. I have seen you, and if you are Death I call your mother a horse-loving whore. Leave me, I will not die!

Basilio Ro spoke it in the tongue of the Abrach.

Santelmo made answer in the Spanish tongue.

You will die very soon, he said.

Yet the strength of knife hand failed him.

[175]

He said to Basilio Ro, A greater knife than mine will kill you.

He looked down once more at the dark shape of the malady sitting bolt upright on the black ground and he had sudden desire to leave the valley. He turned and hurried. He left the bower and started for our camp.

Before he had finished with this recounting, rain began to fall. It came down quietly while dawn grew. Low cloud mantled all the sky, hiding heaven from us, scarfing hilltops with mist.

We spoke little, performing accustomed tasks of breaking camp and making ready to ride. I believe we gave unaccustomed care to the loading and lashing of every pack, to the proper hang of our bridles and the right tightening of our saddles' girths, to the bucklings of the iron harnesses we donned, to the scrutinies we gave the weapons at our belts and in the holsters on our saddles. When we were in readiness to mount,

Don Vito called us together in the rain's quietness by the ashes of a campfire we would not forget.

"You will ride with me now to find a horse thief," Don Vito said. "Wherever and however he may be this morning. I do not go to take him. Or to parley with him. I go to kill him. That will be my own duty, long delayed. You will go with me only to aid as I command and as circumstances may require.

"Santelmo is ready to show us where to go; I want him to ride at my side this morning. Toribio — you take Santelmo's mules. You and Lope will bring the pack train, in regular order, at the rear." He regarded us all, standing there. "Ripalda — this rain is no good for that harquebus. Put it away. Only unlimber that *lazo* of yours and have it in your hand, in case its use is indicated."

Thus ordered we rode down into the Valley of Goodness, toward the river.

I rode with the mules' lead rope in my wet-gloved hand and I thought of Saint John Baptist's Day at Acui-chál. It seemed to me on this phantom morning after the falling of a star that now we were all come as touched with gray strangeness, with spell of mystery insubstantial, as that ensign and that Indian who had arrived with quicksilver and foxfire in gray rainy gloaming. I found my mind suddenly thankful for the mules

[177]

I led, for the tug and slack of the rope in my tensed fingers fastening me and my horse Caobo to some shape and to some evidence of the world's reality on an unreal day in a place bearing a name so cryptic, Valley of Goodness.

Rain fell steadily. Wet stalks of bunch grass grew taller than our stirrups. We crossed an arroyo with a freshet flowing muddy down the throat of the valley. Santelmo led us to higher ground along the valley's shelving side, around the foot of grassy and stone-cluttered hills for more than two leagues.

At a tangled covert of brush on the turn of a little slope the horsemen in our van halted. Lope and I came up with the pack train to where they waited, and we saw the bower.

It was by a ragged field of Indian maize, about two furlongs from us, and not very far from the river's weedy edge. Peering hard, we could detect no sign or stir of life roundabout it. Standing solitary in gray rain, it seemed a place where menace dwelt with desolation. Gray bluffs half shrouded with mist looked down upon it from the other side of the silent river.

Don Vito spoke in low voice. "Santelmo. You will take charge of our pack train. Hold the animals here until I call for you. Understand? Here."

Santelmo nodded.

Don Vito turned to the rest of us. "You four will ride behind me. Spread out with room for any action, and staying well at my back. By that I mean fifty paces at my back as I ride forward. And hear me! I want no foolish melee of five men and horses killing a snake in front of a hut. The deed there requires but one man, and I am he. I will kill the snake. Either luring him from his hole, or destroying him in it. If something else is required I will command you at the time. You each understand? Very well."

He did not draw sword, he had no weapon in his hand. He only touched spur to the gray Tordillo and rode out, in a springy canter as seemingly casual as riding home from a Mass on a Sunday.

I confess I felt not the least casual as I spaced myself behind him, a lance now gripped in my hand *a la jineta,* checking Caobo to the gait of Tordillo in that Sunday cantering! We advanced through quiet strangeness with muffled beat of hooves on wet ground and small patter of rain tapping the iron of our helmets. Half a furlong from the river we passed through the edge of the maize field and we came into open ground, seeing now the dark uncurtained empty doorway of the bower. From the corner of my eye I felt rather than saw Don Teclo with crossbow, Lope with lance, Ripalda with opened loop of *lazo.*

Then came the quick stir and show of life from the dark doorway. With it came the instant shout of Don Vito commanding us to halt; we saw Don Vito's empty right hand held high; we saw Basilio Ro's three slave women; we stared as they half stumbled and half ran at Don Vito with their wavering naked arms upraised. A rod from Tordillo's unmoving hooves they fell down to their knees in obeisance with forlornest cries and touched their foreheads to the earth.

"End it!" came Don Vito's voice. He used Spanish. His eyes never left the doorway of the bower. *"Hear me!"* He raised his voice and he pointed to the bower. "Thy master? *Is he there?"*

"Dead!" We heard the woman's voice. She used the Spanish word. "Dead! Yes, lord, dead!" She raised her arm pointing back at the bower.

"Dead! Dead!" the other two women cried out.

Don Vito's eyes did not leave the bower. "Ensign!" he called. "Come forward." Don Teclo rode to him. "Speak to these women in their tongue. See if they lie. And Lope — " he called. "Go fetch Santelmo and the packs. Ripalda — with that rope — and you, Toribio, with that lance, spread out and ride behind me, with eyes sharp on that doorway!"

"Lord Lieutenant — " came the ensign's reedy voice. "Vito! Let me send this bolt into that doorway!

Let me see how these concubines act when I let fly! Watch them!"

The iron quarrel whistled and we heard the sharp *paf* of its strike within the bower.

"Good?" Don Teclo asked the women. Then he spoke words of Abrach. All three women spoke at once, answering.

"He died," Don Teclo said. "After the terrible light in the darkness and before the coming of day. They knew he would die. A spirit told them."

"We will see," Don Vito said. Now he drew his sword, for the first time.

Ripalda and I rode after him, watching.

He sprang lightly down from his saddle four paces from the silent doorway and without a word he walked into the bower.

Ripalda and I waited.

I felt the tightness of my grip on the lance shaft, I heard the beating of my own heart in the spectral quiet with the patter of the rain on the iron I wore.

Don Vito very suddenly stood facing us again. He looked out at us from the dark of the ghostly door and we heard his voice. "Ro is here. Dead."

I felt my hand ease from its grip on the lance.

Don Vito stood shadowy and unmoving for a moment more; then, as if performing some act of signal fi-

nality, he glanced down to guide the point of his sword
and he returned the blade to its scabbard with a precise
sound of *clatt.*

"Sir," I heard Ripalda say. "You finished him?"

"He was finished, *vaquero!* Death found him. Before I did." Don Vito came out of the doorway. "The
air is better out here, I assure you." He mounted Tordillo. We rode with him to where Don Teclo and the
Indian women stood now, close by Lope and Santelmo
with the pack train.

Don Vito said in calm voice to the ensign, "They
did not lie. Ro is dead." Don Teclo crossed himself.
We all did. "Ensign. What do they say now, seeing
Santelmo here with us?"

"They say little and I cannot judge. But it does not
seem important, Vito! Our Santelmo with that hat and
hinny and brigandine is no spirit from under the ground
at midnight! And I have told him not to speak, in order
that they may not recognize him by his voice!"

"Good enough," Don Vito said. He looked around,
at all of us.

"I would like you to unload the pack that carries the
bright cloth and the trinkets. Something for these woe-
begotten creatures here. When they have had gifts, it
may please them to gather us some ripe ears of that
corn. It may also please them, more importantly, to tell

us exactly how to go — or even go with us — to find their kinsmen and the horses." He looked around again, at all of us. "I do not like this place, sons. As soon as we have performed the Christian duty of burying the body of what was once a Christian, I shall ask you to mount your horses and ride with me, north to find horse tracks."

"The gold, Vito? The gold?"

"I see no gold."

"It is here!"

"Where?"

"There is some in the bower! And the ledge. I have asked the women. It is over there. Beyond the side of that bluff. In that mist. But there!"

"Across that river?"

"Very unfortunately. Across the river. But very close. On the other side."

There was a look of almost infinite dolor in the long, thin, scarred face of Don Teclo Paz. The drooped eye and the wide-open eye both stared intently and stead-ily into the countenance of Don Vito Cantú.

At that moment I was suddenly aware of a new quiet around us, and I realized the rain had ceased fall-ing, for the first time since dawn.

"Teclo Paz," I heard Don Vito saying. "At present, we have tasks on this side of the river. We will do them."

[185]

A gray pit much used for the roasting of *sotol* palm stalks became the grave of Basilio Ro. It was a deep hole not far from the bower; it was already dug; it was ample, after we had cleared the round stones and some of the ashes from it.

I think never were obsequies more strange.

When we were ready to bring the body, Don Vito led us toward the bower. As we approached the door-way he turned and said abruptly, " — Something I neglected to tell you, Ro is not alone in there. I found him with a prisoner, a wretched thing very odd as a pet, and odder yet as a mourner at a bier! It appears to be the size of an eagle, a dark bird alive, held captive and perched in a corner."

"Eagle?" Don Teclo asked.

"Eagle or hawk. The light was poor. I say frankly it gave me a start when I walked in and saw the thing

move a little, and ruffle in the shadow! It might be
that Ro oddly passed the time hawking, in his odd
valley."

"Vito. Something I know! In the Otmaco supersti-
tion the hawk, and more so the eagle, is greatly regarded! The feathers are venerated. Having power,
the wizards believe, to carry incantations to heathen
gods!"

"Gapeseed, Ensign! Say heathen demons."

"That would be more correct, Lord Lieutenant."

"Indeed, and in that case — a Christian act would
be indicated." Don Vito looked at the doorway, fastening the chin strap of his morion, drawing on his
gauntlets. "When I cast it loose, let it come out un-
molested!" He walked into the bower.

Standing outside and clear of the door, we heard a
harsh sound, from a throat not human. There was a
sharp flap, a whirring flutter, then silence.

It was a distressful eagle.

It came in a hesitant ungainly walk from the dim-
ness into the light. It stopped, turned its fierce head, set
its crooked-clawed yellow feet in the mud, swayed its
sick and rusty-feathered body, as if its yellow-rimmed
glaring eyes were unable yet to envisage any meaning
in the wideness of the world. It walked again, the black
tips of its yellow beak parted, in grotesque trial of free-

dom not yet found under a sky not yet discerned.
Then liberation pierced into its heart.

It tried to fly. A rustling labor of great beating wings
brought it free of earth, carried it skimming along the
ground for less than two rods, failing. It scraped down
half-tumbled to a stop, and stood still, its head lifted at
the sky. I have seen few things more affecting, save a
horse rise up from a fall and stand with a broken leg.

"It cannot fly. Shall I kill it?" asked Ripalda.

"No," Don Vito said, standing in the shadowy door.
"It sees the sky."

As he spoke and as we watched, the eagle flew. It
did not soar, but it flew. It rose above the *bosque* of
brush by the river, it flew on, finding strength, learning
the sky.

"See how it goes! Look where it goes!" Don Teclo
Paz cried out.

It went from sight with wings outspread aloft,
around the turn of bluff on the river's far side.

Then Don Vito led us through the door into the
shadowy bower.

The renegade Basilio Ro, whom gray Death had
found, was stretched stiff where the women had laid
him on a low pallet of begrimed deerskins, at the far
end of the windowless room. The body with soul departed lay under a Spanish cloak worn unspeakably

threadbare. Laid upon the cloak was a single large eagle feather. The face of Basilio Ro was exposed. We looked down at it.

"Dead eagle," Ripalda said in the silence. It seemed enough to say. Don Vito reached down and pulled the cloak over the face. The eagle feather did not fall from the cloak; Don Vito with the back of his gloved hand deliberately brushed the feather to the floor.

A smell of Death or of evil or of an eagle's sick droppings hung in my nostrils. We wrapped the cloak and deerskins as a shroud, abhorring what we touched, and made it secure with cactus fiber strings Lope found hanging on the doorpost. Then we lifted the burden in its reasty soiled integument and carried it with some shuffling awkwardness to the *sotol* pit.

The three women watched us. If they mourned they made no outward sign, standing silent at a little distance, fingering the bright new cotton cloth that now girdled and bodiced them, and toying with the strings of glass beads around their necks.

"Such ceremony as we lack here — it needs no comment," Don Vito said. "Let the body down into the grave." We used Ripalda's *lazo* for it.

When it was done and the rope was drawn out and we stood there by the side of the pit, Don Vito said, "We need make no mouthings for propriety's sake. But it would harm none of us here, and might aid, each to say an Our Father — " he stopped to cast a glance around, inquiring. Don Teclo Paz was not present, or in sight. Santelmo sat with the horses a hundred *varas* away. The women watched us silently. "No matter — " he said. " — Our Father, who art in heaven," he led us, and we prayed it, and at the end we made our Crosses. "Now cover it over. I will help," Don Vito said.

We put a number of the heavy round rocks on top the fill and it was a decent grave we made for an unshriven man who defied Death to find him.

When we were done and had put on our helmets and picked up our camp spades and were ready to go to the horses, we saw Don Teclo Paz coming from the bower. His spurs clinked with each hustling step. He carried in his arms two lumpy sacks manifestly heavy. "Lord Father mine!" the reedy voice quavered.

Near us he let the sacks down carefully to the ground. They were of thick leather and they were all splotched with eagle droppings.

"Gold!" The eyes in the dolorous face were beady with a fantast's gleam. He untwisted the cord on a sack, opened it, brought out a handful of broken rock crusty with glint of yellow shine. "Gold, my sons! In our hands. We have come to it. Rich beyond dream!"

"Hear me, Ensign," spoke Don Vito. "While you were rummaging among eagle cruts in a charnel house, we buried Ro. Shall we bury his gold also? Now?"

"Eh? Did I hear you? — Christ save us, are you mad, Vito Cantú?"

"You heard me. I am not mad. Basilio Ro was. Are you now?"

"Mad! Be so kind as to explain what madness there may be in locating — here — now — at last — on that ledge under the crown of that bluff over there — eh? — the richest mine of gold in the Indies! *Mad?*"

"I only asked. And without anger. Put the mineral back into the bag, Teclo Paz. Tie it securely. Cherish it as you wish. I would rather see it buried. Here. But if you insist otherwise, there will be room in the packs for it. Carry it, as reward for this journey you have made. It is yours. Hear me, all yours! Not ours. Nor is that ledge across the river ours!" Don Vito Cantú looked around at each of us, full in the face. "I speak for myself. I want no part of this place, or anything in it, or anything near it! Teclo Paz. Old Carrier of the Banner. Old companion-at-arms. Old Ibarra man. I told you at Acuichál my purpose for riding here. You knew it then, you know it now. It is not to find gold." He looked around at us again. "I have spoken for myself. Without presumption, I believe I may also speak

[197]

for three men who ride with me: Ripalda — *vaquero!* Lope — *domador!* Toribio — *jinete!* We do not peck at rocks, three hundred leagues from the nearest *gobernación,* for such riches as we may hope for, and want most! It happens that we have another kind of work, for another kind of riches. Which we find not in a strongbox, but on a pasture of grass."

Don Teclo Paz devoted his attention to tying the cord tightly around the closed mouth of the sack. His hands trembled.

Sunlight in those moments touched down, casting shadows sharp and clear upon the ground at our feet.

"Thus it is," came the reedy voice. "And I have a further business here. Which I will pursue, with you or without you!"

"Ill-starred business! As Ro found it! And as Ro left it!"

"Hear *me* now, Evaristo Rodrigo Cantú. I am not Ro!" Don Teclo Paz stood up, facing Don Vito Cantú. "It was I who learned of this valley and what it held and it was I who told you! It was I who brought you here. It was I who brought you in all good faith, serving you with all that I have, which is little, but which is not unfaithful. You would ride now without me? Without guide, without advantage of interpreter in the Indian tongue — to find, if you can, and to *take,* if you can, a horse herd from a tribe of Indians able and willing to fight you in all their numbers! *Vah!* What about madness? Who is mad? So reflect for a moment: the true mine of the true Quivira! Is this such a matter of madness, or is it rather a matter of interest, to any old Ibarra man who once served Francisco and *yet* serves Diego de Ibarra, both of whom pecked rocks for riches, riches very substantial! You would ask me to leave this strange valley now for the second time in my life without — without setting my feet upon the great ledge of gold! Before I ride north with you, Vito Cantú, I must go and I must see that ledge! Here is mineral from it, yes, two sacks full, gathered by a dead man's hand. I must see the lode. I must know it is there, accursed or blessed! I must know that I have found it. That we have found it. Then I will be content, for the days left to me, however many, however few. And I consider it unlikely, in the nature of all things seen and unseen, that the Lord God Almighty plans to let me ride out thrice to this world's edge! No one knows its great size, its great solitude, better than I. I have never owned a strongbox, such as you mentioned. I have owned only hope. I beg you, Vito, to make our camp by the river. For this one night. Give me this one afternoon to go with Santelmo, to the crossing half a league downriver, then to the ledge. It shines there now, as

[199]

Santelmo said it would, after a rain! We will return to camp before dark. Tomorrow morning we will ride north, to find the Abrach and the horses."

"Well — Ensign — " Don Vito made answer slowly. "You persuade me. Not that it is wise! But that it is better to be unwise than to be ungrateful — or to seem ungrateful — to you. Go with Santelmo. Satisfy yourself. We will make the camp, there where you see those trees. I ask the favor of your return to camp by nightfall."

"Before then!" Don Teclo's thin lips shaped a smile in his weathered beard. "Sweet Carambola!"

The three women did bring us ears of ripe corn to parch. Then, pointing upriver to the rude huts and narrow fields left deserted by the valley's people, they fell to their knees and asked if they might go now to where they had dwelt formerly, and be released from their bondage at the bower. Don Vito gave them some dried strips of our venison and let them go freely as they desired.

Lope took the horses and mules to graze the tall couch grass on a hillside. Don Vito, much withdrawn into his own thought, made the fire, occupied himself with shucking corn and putting on the iron pot of beans to stew with a few pods of *chile* and chunks of the dried meat he cut with his dagger. Ripalda and I ranged the packs, set up camp, gathered firewood, brought water from the river.

We were hungry, we were weary, and we felt no ease.

I noticed that I was not the only one to turn and gaze, more than once, for some sign of moving figure which I could not find on the stone-dotted slope below the crown of the rounded bluff downriver.

Long before dusk I expected and I greatly desired the good sight of our ensign on Clarín, our Indian with his hat and his hinny, riding again the edge of the *bosque*, coming at us from around the bend of the river. They did not appear. At nightfall they did not return.

We supped by our fire, waiting, listening. The bright Star of Evening went down behind the bluffs. A myriad fainter stars all securely fastened in the firmament began their shining from the sky's velvet vault.

[201]

We hoped for another point of light, some fire, some sign from the slope's dark face beyond the black line of the silent river. None showed.

I had the first watch. The horses, feeling the absence of Clarín and the hinny, stood restless at their picket, sharing the disquiet that seemed to flicker with the shadows of our fire.

The blaze burned low; Lope rekindled it. I heard Don Vito speak to him and Ripalda: "I do not expect them now until the light of morning. They were detained, in some manner. I find my own uneasiness unreasonable. Both of them have spent ten thousand nights in wilderness, and many of them without supper! Take some sleep now, until your watches. Mine is the *modorra*." Stripped to the undress of hose and jerkin, he spread his blanket, placed his sword, settled himself for sleep. Lope and then Ripalda followed his example.

Firelight died in the quiet; the air was very still. My eyes were stinging with sleepiness and I was gazing, to hold them open, at the curve of the stars in the Scorpion's tail when I heard the sudden sound from the darkness downriver, the peculiar crying neigh of Santelmo's hinny. The horses and mules jerked snorting — one of the mules gave a quick-breathed high bray.

"Here they come!" I cried out. Don Vito, Ripalda,

Lope were already on their feet; I was as tense as the horses I sought to soothe.

We heard hoofbeats. Ripalda trotted out into the dark, toward the sound.

"*Hei-i?*" Don Vito challenged.

There was silence, then Ripalda's voice, "The *burdégano* — the hinny — only the hinny!"

"God's Mother Mary! — Lope, throw wood on that fire!" Don Vito ran out where Ripalda had gone.

They came back, into the flicker of new blaze. They came leading the rearing, lathered hinny by its halter rope. "*Ah* ha — " Don Vito quieted, taking harsh grip on the noseband. The hinny stood, trembling. The saddle was empty.

Don Vito grabbed up the end of the halter rope and held it toward the fire to see better. "The hinny was tethered. And broke the rope. And came to camp dragging it." Now Don Vito's voice was steady, cool. "Very well, Ripalda. Saddle your dun. Lope, bring my gray here to the light." Don Vito sat down on his blanket and pulled on his boots.

When the two horses were readied, Don Vito buckled on sword and dagger, armed his saddle with the holstered wheellock, hung the key, the powder flask, ball pouch and an extra match cord around his neck, and asked Ripalda, "How are you armed now?"

"Rope and knife."

"Good." Don Vito turned to us. "You two, Lope and Toribio, are here to tend the horses and to guard this camp until we return. Be alert!"

They mounted and rode into the darkness.

We unsaddled the hinny, finding no mark or clue to disaster on the animal or the saddle. Lope took the hinny to water at the river, and it drank long. We restored it to its mule chum at the picket line, and we built up the fire. To busy ourselves we got out the harquebuses, powder flasks, balls, wads, match cords, and even the swines. We sat in the stillness a long time, wondering to ourselves, listening.

" — Did you hear that?" I asked Lope.

"Yes! Firearm! The *pistola de arzón* — "

"You think so?"

"One discharge."

"Yes. Listen!"

There was only silence.

"You think it was a signal to us?"

"He mentioned no signal."

We sat wordless, worried — weary.

I half drowsed and I knew that I did and in my ache of fatigue I would shake my head and rouse myself to find more wood for the fire.

The blue-bright star overhead had moved four hand-

breadths down from the zenith when we heard *"Hei-i!"* from the darkness by the river.

Don Vito and Ripalda rode to us and got down from their horses — weary.

I saw darkly what Don Vito Cantú carried in his hand: the morion of Don Teclo Paz, the Christian hat of the Indian Santelmo. My heart sank.

"You did — find them?"

"We found the hats."

"Not more?"

"We found Clarín. *Satanás y sus cuernos!* Neck broken, clawed, gut torn, partly eaten. A lion!"

"But — Don Teclo? Santelmo? Where?"

"Only this! As it appears: this afternoon they came to the crossing place. They decided, for an un-known reason, to leave their horses on this side. They tied them there. They left their hats on the riverbank, possibly because they believed they might have to swim part of the crossing. I do not know. I know they did not come back to the animals they left on this side of the water. I know that when the lion attacked our Clarín, the hinny broke loose from tether and came to tell us! As to our ensign or the Indian — we will see when day comes!"

"The firearm we heard, Don Vito? Was it for a signal? For Don Teclo to hear?"

"It was for the lion! It was there, eating! And the damnable shot missed, as usual, in the vile dark!"

With dawn growing, Lope was left alone to tend the horses and guard the camp; I think only because I had ability to swim was I ordered to ride with Don Vito and Ripalda. We went at a long trot downriver to the crossing. Buzzards already had found Clarín. They rose up and circled wheeling overhead when we came to the place. Our horses were very fearful.

My tears fell, though I believe I hid them.

"Ripalda." Don Vito spoke. "That zebra-legged dun is the strongest swimmer we have and you are the best tracker I know. How do you feel about making a proof of this crossing and then cutting for sign along the other bank?"

"Command us, Don Vito."

"After you have found tracks showing that they in

fact arrived on the other side, Toribio and I will cross
and we will all go tracking, wherever it leads."

"If there are tracks, I will find them. And follow
them."

"I am sure of it. There is another thing also: if there
are no tracks over there."

"It has entered my mind. Surveying this water."
Ripalda was afoot, studying the crossing.

"You believe it dangerous?"

"It requires caution. But I have crossed uglier wa-
ters! So has Vaquero. We swam the Mesquitál together." Ripalda took off his morion. "Watch us go,
Don Vito." He began to pull off his boots.

"If there are no tracks over there — " Don Vito
frowned. "If they were pulled under and perished. In
such case, Ripalda, you will be over there to search
down the stream on that side. While Toribio and I ride
this bank."

"As you order it, Don Vito."

Ripalda tied his morion, boots, breeches and bridle
on his saddle. Leading his horse by the light tie rope
on the halter, he coaxed it into the water; they waded
for a dozen *varas* before the channel made it necessary
for them to swim. Ripalda stayed close to the dun's
shoulder on the upstream side, talking to his companion, and it was good to watch their steadiness as they

[209]

moved through the water. Past mid-channel they both thrashed, momentarily caught and swung in some quick suckhole grip of current, but they straightened strongly, went on to firm footing in shallows and strode out together on dry shore. The dun was a noble horse.

From this crossing place Ripalda rode the riverbank, both downstream and upstream, for three hundred vigilant *varas*. He found no footprint, no sign of any kind, to show that Don Teclo Paz or the Indian Santelmo had come out of the water.

Then for two sorrowful leagues downstream we rode searching the two sides of the silent river in its desolate cañon. We examined every riverbank twist and shoal, every clot of drift and float, every clump and pocket of waterside brush, weed, trash along the way. We saw nothing. We gave up hope of finding the bodies delivered from that brown river in that wilderness of stone.

It was far into afternoon when we came back again upstream to the crossing place. The buzzards flapped up, flying from the feasting we disturbed. They wheeled over us while Don Vito and I waited and Ripalda with his admirable dun swam the river again to our side.

"They made no crossing, Don Vito," Ripalda said. "If they did, their feet were in air. They made no print on the ground."

Ripalda put on his clothes, bridled his horse, adjusted the wet girth of his saddle. The buzzards circled, patiently. In the silence I could hear the buzzing of the flies on Clarín.

Ripalda was mounted and ready to ride when Don Vito finally turned his eyes from gazing up at the shady slope under the bleak crown of the bluff on the other side of the Great North River. He looked down the river and he spoke, it seemed more to himself than to us. "So we leave it. The ensign and his Indian." Then he spoke to us. "God rest them. Where the streets are all paved with gold." He turned Tordillo upstream and touched spur.

Lope greeted us at camp with a look of infinite and unspeakable relief. When we rode in, Don Vito did not get down from his saddle. "Lope — " he called, "did those wretched women of Ro come to this camp today?"

"No, sir! I have been alone."

"You saw any sign of them up there at that *rancheria?* Cooksmoke or the like?"

"Nothing, Don Vito. It has been quiet! Too quiet! God the Father, how quiet!"

Don Vito looked around. "The three of you can make some noise — cooking supper. Graze the horses. Prepare for another night here. While there is light, I will make a brief scout of that dead village."

He returned to camp in the dusk. "The women are gone," he said. "I cannot say that I blame them! Though I hoped they might help us, somewhat, finding the people at the River of the Cows."

There were four of us, not six, preparing to ride from the valley: we rearranged and rebalanced all the packs.

Don Vito Cantú with no comment took a clean kerchief and in it wrapped the morion of Teclo Paz; with it he wrapped the frazzled yet oddly intrepid hat of Santelmo with its copper Cross and forlorn feather. Wrapped and tied, they were packed in a pannier to go where we might go.

Then Don Vito gathered together all other effects belonging to Teclo Paz and to the Indian. The treasured nugget wrapped in the wrinkled silk was there; so were the two very heavy leather bags from the bower. He made a bundle of everything. When it was lashed tight together, bound around with the broken length of rope from the hinny's halter, he carried it to the riverbank and swung it into the brown water, where it splashed sharply and sank. He walked back to us with no comment, and we made none.

I recount this to indicate the character of the man who led us north from the Valley of Goodness, Valle de Bondad.

Cast now into an endless enormity of wilderness trod by no men save unknown savages since the beginning of the world, we made our way without guide or information, without knowing where we were, knowing only what our leader sought: the tracks of Christians' horses fallen into heathens' hands.

We did not know nor could we conceive what course of action Don Vito Cantú would employ if he found what he sought; he did not tell us. We knew only that we were four armed men horseback with a pack train, come three hundred lonely leagues to take, somehow, a whole herd of horses from the wild hands of many Indians.

It seemed a chimera, though we said nothing.

We found pasturage plentiful. Water we found only by sharpness of eye, by Ripalda's *vaquero* cunning concerning terrain, and by God's grace. One night our camp was dry; our horses suffered having to carry us nearly twenty leagues between waterings, for the first time since we had left Acuichál.

Bearing always north, our way took us first through harsh and broken uplands, with timbered sierras in hazy distance out upon our left, westward. We passed then across long basins cut by shallow ravines and hemmed by jumbles of hills. From these we issued out upon almost level prairies edged by rimrock on flat-topped mesas and tilted ridges.

In a country that seemed to mourn its own solitude, in a dismal land of tawny soil, gray stone, thorny brush, six days and seventy uncertain leagues from the Great North River, we came upon the ribbon of green chaparral lining the crumbly banks of the drab stream: River of the Cows, flowing sluggish, deep, narrow, edged with green scum, from northwestward. Though Ripalda was able to throw a *lazo* to the other bank, the swimming of the narrow water cost us and our animals

some exertion; we made our camp on the north bank and we remained there for a day to shoe horses, recruit ourselves and repair gear. Don Vito ordered and supervised us also in another rearrangement of our pack-loads, somewhat to my puzzlement at the time. All articles most essential to us, our utensils, commissary, arms, powder, camp tools and the like were sorted and packed for carrying in the panniers and wrapped top-loads on our three pack horses. All else, composed largely of extras, spares, oddments, bundles of bright cloth, packages of gauds, trifles and beads, were made into very light packs indeed for the backs of the three mules and the hinny.

"Convenient for the Abrach, when we meet them. And in accord with the old saying at Ronda, 'Gifts break rocks,' " was all Don Vito told us. We did not inquire more from him.

The very first day of our journeying beyond the River of the Cows we saw no Abrach, but we saw a long trailing cloud of dust low on the plain's edge to the east. We rode toward it, we stared, we marveled: it was a drifting great herd of the wild cows of the North, thousands, a dark brown and very wooly on the shoulders and forequarters and heads, humpbacked, as large and more agile than Castilian bulls, black-horned, with beards like billy goats, and meager tails with only a tag of bristly hair at the tip. The herd's acrid smell came downwind heavily, the multitude of hooves made unending murmur.

Our horses and mules were much enspirited, but we calmed them and rode close. Don Vito knocked down a young bull with a shot of the wheellock firearm and finished the beast with a lance. We butchered it out where it fell, and we loaded ribs and a quarter on one of the lightly packed mules. That night at camp by the river we found the meat delicious like beef, with far more fat and juice than venison.

I shall not forget the vastness and the quietness of the sky that night as we stood our watches and the coyote wolves cried. The Mariner's Star stood higher in the north than ever I had seen it — or would see again.

Next day, moving north, we saw horse tracks.

Iba-rra

We came to the lip of a long slow rise on the plain and very suddenly looked over the break, at the hollow with the pool of water and the encampment of the Abrach there in outstretched shadows of late afternoon. We saw the cone-shaped tents of hide, moving figures, thin smokes of cookfires at end of day; we spied the horse pen of crooked stakes and piled brush: we spied horses in it, not two hundred *varas* ahead of us! Our own animals were snorting.

"We have the luck!" Don Vito's voice was low; his eyes darted. "Before they see us and send archers — hear me carefully and quickly. *Lope* — remain here with the pack horses. *Ripalda* — when I call for you to bring the three mules and the hinny, *bring* them! *Toribio* — if and when I call for you to ride to me — come immediately! All of you now — eyes sharp and God with us!"

Don Vito shouted out and waved his morion high in his right hand. Our animals were much excited, neighing, scenting mares' reek for the first time in many weeks. Savage figures ran shouting between the tents, dogs barked. Don Vito, leaving us, touched spur and rode quick to meet the gather of the shouting crowd.

Ten paces from us he put Tordillo into an abrupt curvet leap, and another, then another, with helmet doffed. The Abrach stood still. Tordillo went into an advancing *levade*, pawing air. The Abrach quieted, gaping. Tordillo back-stepped, turned, back-stepped, turned, made two wide and graceful circlings in side-ward dancing; then once more advanced toward the en-campment's edge, in noble display of the swaying and high-lifted Spanish Step, to halt and make salute with a bow of arched neck ten paces from the crowd. Stand-ing still, Tordillo gave a sudden shrill neigh, clearly for the penned mares, but of very great effect as a flourish. The Abrach clapped their hands!

Riding Caobo to within fifty *varas* of distance from Don Vito Cantú now, I watched him dismount, make the hand sign of peace and friendship, and call out for the chief *sibiye* or cacique present among the people.

With a painted hide robe about his waist the *sibiye* stepped forward, making the same sign Don Vito had made, and others. When he had done this, Don Vito with courtliness pointed to the brand on Tordillo's hip, the Cross-Enflanked I, and with his finger he then wrote it large in the air, making it very clear.

I saw the *sibiye* nod, and heard him call out to some of his people, directing them: and very soon I saw being led through the crowd and to Don Vito — stud horses, five, six, seven of them, two of them little more than weaned colts. I watched Don Vito examine each one, and I saw that he found the Cross-Enflanked I branded on three of the older stallions, for he would point to them, and write the brand in the air, and the *sibiye* would nod and write it himself.

Watching, I could see that it seemed an agreeable thing to Don Vito and the *sibiye* both, for they began much cordial making of signs with their hands, and counting of fingers, and nodding, and shaking their heads. It was a sight, with the people all standing intent, with dogs all ceased of their barking, and all at respectful distance from the great Tordillo, who stood planted with propriety, head restless and high, nostrils flared!

Then all heard Don Vito shout, "Ripalda!" and make motion for him to advance.

Ripalda with a stony face rode forward, leading the three mules and the hinny tailed up by their halter ropes in file behind him; he halted them well before they came near the seven studs, or the *sibiye* standing with Don Vito and Tordillo in front of the crowd.

All watched while Don Vito showed the *sibiye* that the mules and the hinny indeed did not carry the Cross-Enflanked I on the hip, and that indeed all four were male animals and strong; the *sibiye* himself examined the genitals to see that all were evident *machos,* and nodded. Don Vito with easy hand unlashed one of the mule packs and setting the panniers to the ground invited the *sibiye* to explore their contents. The *sibiye* pulled out bright-dyed kerchiefs, a box full of glittering little pieces of mirror glass, four iron bit rings, a shiny brass buckle, a bolt of yellow muslin, which clearly pleased him, for he allowed his mien to show it.

Don Vito took the lead rope from Ripalda's hand and with courtesy most formal put it into the hand of the *sibiye.* In response, the *sibiye* spoke to those seven Abrach who each stood holding a stallion by a hide strap around the neck and nose, and the *sibiye* then solemnly gestured to Don Vito, making it known that horses to the number of seven were now traded!

"Take them slowly, Ripalda," called Don Vito. "Ease them out. For the love of Blessed Mary, herd them easy — you and Lope, and take them with the pack horses, take them."

Thus smoothly and peaceably did Don Vito Cantú

trade our mules and the hinny and everything on their backs, in exchange for the Indians' entire stud stock — all seven sources for procreation and increase of the herd now taken away! It seemed masterfully ingenious, as I sat there on my horse Caobo watching Ripalda smile in his black beard and drive all the stallions from the Abrach camp.

I did not yet know the measure of Don Vito Cantú's daring.

"Toribio — " he called out to me. "Come riding to us — put Caobo in his prettiest gait!"

I rode to him in a most decorous high-stepping single-foot, not straightaway but circling in a figure-eight for ample show, and I drew up halting in formal salute. Don Vito indicated another salute for the *sibiye*, which I gave, with flourish. Then pointing toward the mare pen, Don Vito made known by signs to the *sibiye* that he and I both wished to enjoy the privilege of seeing all the mares — and permission for the great gray Tordillo to enter with the mares in their enclosure!

The Abrach cacique's solemn face showed some surprise, then indecision shaded by curiosity. Then — confronted with Don Vito's courtliness standing by the noble Tordillo — the *sibiye* assented: I think surely for some advantage of majestic instruction from Don

Vito in the equine arts, for it was perfectly clear that the Abrach cow hunters were only green apprentices yet in the handling of horse stock.

Instruction came in fullest measure! And not only to the Abrach.

Don Vito Cantú took the bridle off Tordillo and, handing it up to me, told me to tie it securely on the apple of my saddle. He sprang then upon the rein-free Tordillo, and grasping lightly a lock of Tordillo's mane said to me and Caobo, "Guide us now, letting us go by your side, to the entrance of the enclosure — " and we did so.

There he indicated to the *sibiye* that he would enter into the pen riding Tordillo without rein, if the gate were opened for him. It was done, and Tordillo carrying his august master went in among the mares, where, by some power over horses which other men do not possess, Don Vito Cantú reinless rode the excited stud straight and controlled to the far end of the mare pen! He quietly dismounted and came around to stand in front of Tordillo, speaking with great softness and holding his hand gently and still upon the stallion's nose. Then Don Vito Cantú with all eyes upon him turned away from his horse and walked very deliberately, with his hand still raised, the length of the pen to the raw-hide strap gate. Opening it and turning calmly as he did so, he faced Tordillo again. The gray stallion stood planted where Don Vito Cantú had stationed him, as still as a horse cast of silver!

In this moment of his life and his power as a horse-man, Evaristo Rodrigo Cantú called out a single word, *"Now!"* and whistled sharply two notes into the star-tled air.

The stud horse gathered, rocked back, then plunged. Released into the wreak of his own nature in that in-stant, biting, striking, rearing, he shoved the sudden milling tangle of his mares into the gate now flung open wide by Don Vito Cantú and they lunged out in wild pounding from the pen, all streaming away with the shrilling stallion after them headlong. Before I or the *sibiye* or any dumbfounded Indian witness could fetch our minds, Don Vito Cantú without stirrup had vaulted up behind me on Caobo! He gripped my iron-encir-cled waist, his voice rasped at my ear: "Now *go* with spur! *Go following Tordillo and the mares of Guati-mape! Hei!*" he bellowed with all his lungs — "Ripal-l-lda! Lope! Bring all! All! To the River of the Cows! *Follow us and Tordillo!* Then-n to *Acui-i-chá-ál!*"

A Spanish soldier never shouted a *Santiago* louder.

We hurled ourselves from the Abrach, leaving them too startled, it seemed, to mount their packsaddled mules for pursuit until it was too late. We left them too dismayed to send anything but a dozen arrows of desperation at our backs as we went flying farther and farther from range in sundown light. We went driving all the horse stock, every head, *machos y hembras*, studs and mares! We took them without the shedding of blood Christian or heathen or equine, and we came to the River of the Cows before dark.

There in the dusk Don Vito, riding double with me yet on Caobo, calmed Tordillo in the midst of his lathered and winded mares. I was able to flip an easy loop of my *lazo*, holding him. Then Don Vito bridled him again, soothed him, mounted him, and said to him: "Well done, Gray One. You are like your grandfather."

We rode all the night, putting distance between us and the Abrach, in starlight driving three pack horses, seven loose studs, fifteen loose mares with four unweaned foals, league after league down the north bank of the River of the Cows. We found a place to cross safely about noon the next day, and pressing on, without any pause until nightfall, we commenced the long journey, pointing our horse herd southward, homeward to Acuichál.

Hacienda of Acuichál
Nueva Vizcaya
Day of San Rafael
Year 1580 of Our Lord

To the very excellent Señor Don Diego de Ibarra
Honored Sir:

I have the privilege to inform you that five days past the licentiate from the *gobernación* at Guadiana, Don Rafael Arrillaga, with two authorized notaries arrived here with all necessary documents and powers to place me in full possession of title to the livestock pastures denominated Acuichál.

As sign of my possession and in the presence of the licentiate and other required witnesses, I pulled up grass, spilled water, broke sticks and performed all ceremonial formalities; whereupon the documents were signed, certified and delivered in a copy to me, my heirs and my assigns, for protection as provided by law.

I gave to Don Rafael before he left us at this house the gift of a very good saddle horse, well-reined, to take him on his journeys henceforth.

I have no means whatever to express to you, noble patron and friend, the gratitude I feel for your generosity in this gift of land I have named Acuichál. Know only, as I believe you must, that I am your obedient and faithful servant until death.

This letter will be placed in your hand by our esteemed Toribio de Ibarra, who returns to Coyoacán at my request in order to convey my thanks and also to bring you information concerning a journey we made into the North.

> *Item:* I count it most fortunate that we had returned here and were present as legally required when the Licentiate Arrillaga arrived, for we had no advance notice whatsoever concerning any date of his official arrival at Acuichál.

As to the journey: we were absent from Acuichál horseback for eighty-three days and we rode a distance of more than seven hundred Spanish leagues, a considerable part of this in wilderness unknown and unseen previously by Christians. We were a company of six men only, but very well mounted, and with a pack train to carry all that we required.

I believe I would be correct if I stated that no such expedition has ever been attempted by other persons, official or unofficial, since the discovery of these Indies. Our horses made it possible. They took us where we went and they brought us home.

I regret to report that I saw there in the North nothing of any fine cities, intelligent peoples or rich kingdoms. I believe these are fables, existing in imagination but not in geography. The only true wonder which I have seen with my own eyes is the vastness of the terrain. It is enormous. Much of it is rough, dry, barren. Some of it is very well suited for pasture of livestock in some future epoch, if ever the populace of this New Spain be sufficiently increased for it.

Mineral exists, unfound. Our Toribio returns to you not only charged with delivery of these written words but with delivery, to you alone, of an accurate verbal account of all circumstances by which we were led close to what seems to be the location of gold. The circumstances and the location both appeared to me so unreasonably touched with forbidding augury that I found no desire either to explore or to exploit what might be there. I am no prospector. In that connection, two

members of our company — the thin Ensign Teclo
Paz whom you will remember, and a baptized Indian
of the North who was his guide faithfully — were lost
to us by drowning in a tragedy of mistaken judgment;
for which I feel the blame, and for which I sorrow.

As to the better results of the venture: in all those
seven hundred leagues we lost but a single horse, killed
by a panther lion. Moreover, we came home with
twenty-six head of Ibarra horse stock which we did not
have when we set out! These were the survivors of that
herd which was viciously stolen from Guatimape by the
condemned traitor Basilio Ro, during Don Francisco's
final sickness. We found these horses in the hands of
savages who follow the wild cows on the endless plains!
I trust Toribio to give you such detail as you may desire
in reference to the manner in which these horses were
retrieved and all brought safely to Acuichál.

In returning homeward we crossed the cart trace
which now leads from San Martín northward, and we
by chance encountered a *conducta* with a company of
carters and some settlers traveling to the Santa Bárbola
district with supplies. The official in charge happened to
be the Captain Sánchez Chamuscado, the same who is
commissioned to lead that party of missionary friars
north next year. I was able to offer him the benefit of
information concerning the best route for them to take.

He will find it useful, if he heeds it. With him were
some of the horses he has procured for the exploration.
I say he will be wishing for some better ponies before
he is done.

Since I have seen the type of heathens who live by
hunting the wild cows on the wild plains of the North,
I hold even stronger conviction than I held before, in
reference to the control of our horse stock here at this
most distant frontier of New Spain. We have here a
huge, natural and splendid country for the strong nourishment and immense increase of horses. I have done
and shall continue to do all I can to keep our horses in
Christian hands. Yet it seems planted in the very nature of things that there will be a time when strong,
cunning, brave Indians, of which there are many, will
find means to possess horses and breed horses and ride
horses and make war on horseback. In the day when
tribes of warriors, hunters and thieves are no longer
afoot, in the day when we see our noble animals used
between the naked legs of painted savages: in that day,
near or distant, I say this realm of our Sacred Cesarean
Catholic Majesty will face woes it cannot count.

Meanwhile, we accomplish what we can.

I send our Toribio to you now feeling that it is
proper to do so, yet admitting sadness. We shall feel
his absence. I would consider him singularly suitable

to represent you, if it be that you cannot travel here, in that tally and accounting of the Acuichál livestock which we should make, you and I, in the spring season of the coming year. I make bold to hope that you will send him, for we shall await him. Our old saddler ser‑geant Gonzalo Duro designates Toribio now as an au‑thentic Northerner, as we say here, and fondly. Myself, I designate him: horseman, *jinete*, of the proven mark.

May God Our Lord preserve you for many years. I kiss the hand of your Excellency and sign myself your servant in fealty and devotion,

eVarIsTO   rod°·   CANTÚ